TI Part Number 1014828-4

MAKING TRACKS INTO PROGRAMMING

A step-by-step learning guide
to the power, ease and fun
of using your **TI Programmable 57**

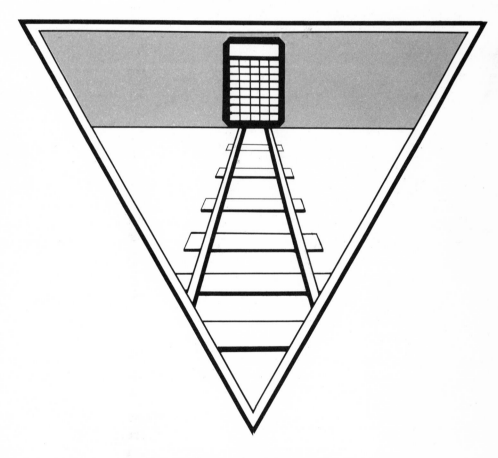

A complete owner's manual
for the **TI Programmable 57.**

This book was developed by:

The Staff of the Texas Instruments Learning Center:
Dr. Ralph A. Oliva, Educational Software Director
Joe E. Poyner
M. Dean LaMont

With contributions by:
Danny J. Enzone
Thomas E. Merrow
Peter L. Bonfield
Arthur L. Norrington Jr.
Henry M. Meltzer
Johnny M. Barrett

and

The Staff of the University of Denver Mathematics Laboratory:
Dr. Ruth I. Hoffman, Director
Sr. Margaret Grace Elsey, Ph.D.
Lucille P. Grogan
Robert L. Kaes
Louis D. Kovari
James F. Reed
Michael R. Zastrocky

With contributions by:
Capt. John Warner, USAF

Artwork and layout were coordinated and executed by:
Schenck, Plunk & Deason

Cover design by:
Gaither & Davy Design Studio Inc.

ISBN 0-89512-004-6

Library of Congress Catalog Number: 77-79825

TABLE OF CONTENTS

CONTENTS DIAGRAM

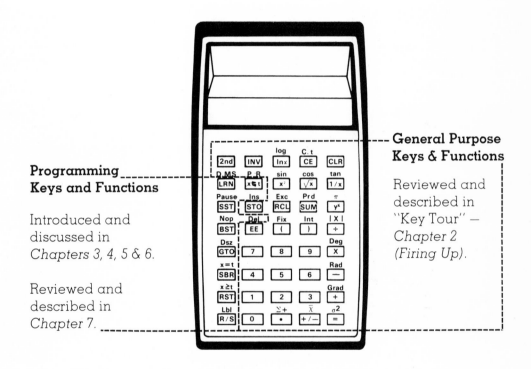

A FIRST LOOK AT THE TI PROGRAMMABLE 57

The calculator you're about to begin using is really straight out of the "world of science fiction" of just a few months ago. Only the most recent advancements in solid-state technology have made it possible to put such an easy and fun-to-use bundle of power right in the palm of your hand.

EASY TO USE

A quick look at your calculator will tell you that it's packed with lots of keys and features. Introducing you, step-by-step, to each of these keys and features is one primary purpose of this book. Above and beyond all these features, however, is one overriding characteristic that was designed into your *TI Programmable 57* right from the start: *It's easy to use.* It's easy to make it do many things that can be enormously helpful in your schoolwork, extremely powerful in your career, and a lot of fun in your everyday life. It's designed to be a working tool that, working together with the information contained in this book, becomes a system for problem-solving and a key to discovery. We hope you'll enjoy using and exploring with it.

STARTING AT THE TOP

In learning about your machine, let's start right off with the nameplate — and a brief look at why we called it what we did:

TI — The calculator is built by *Texas Instruments Incorporated.*

PROGRAMMABLE — As you will be seeing in a few seconds, it is easy to "teach" your machine to help in solving problems, evaluating formulas and building "models" of your world. You can lay down a set of "Tracks" that the machine will follow as it solves a problem. A word, recognizable to some folks, that describes such a machine is already around: "Programmable". This machine, however, is a new thing — with a whole new, easy approach. So if "programmable" is a word that scares you — don't let it. Using your "57" is a cinch.

57 — This machine is the latest in a growing family of Texas Instruments programmable calculators, and it's "following in the footsteps" of another machine, our *SR-56.* The 57 is an even easier machine to use — designed for especially straightforward use.

How Does It Work?

Simple! For starters, take out the calculator and check out the "heft" of this little device. Light, isn't it? That's because most of the important things inside this calculator are handled with a device that the folks at TI call a "SOAP" bar. (More on that later.)

Now, turn it on! A zero in the display tells you that you're ready for action. (If the zero doesn't come on, or the display seems to be doing "funny" things, don't worry. The battery just needs charging. Turn the machine off, plug in your charger and wait a few minutes; then you'll be set to go.)

Let's get right into it with a simple example.
Imagine this situation:
You've just won a rather weird award from a major radio station. You'll be given 2¢! This money will be doubled every day for three weeks (21 days). *OR* — you can have $5000 in cash immediately. You have two minutes to make a decision — the announcer is waiting. (This is actually an "old and classic" problem. Watch how your calculator helps.)

Basically, you can have your machine read out for you just how your money will "grow". Here's how:

Over on the upper left hand corner of your machine, one row down from the top, is a key that is the real "jewel":
it's labelled LRN ———————➤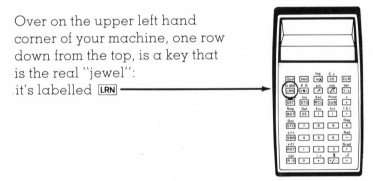

This is the "learn" key, and when you press it one time, your calculator begins to learn and remember whatever you put in next. When you press LRN again, you're telling the calculator that you've "taught" it everything you want it to know for now. The calculator stops learning at this point, but remembers all the steps you taught it. (The LRN key is like an "ON/OFF" button for teaching your calculator to do things.)

So press LRN. (At this point your display changes to **00 00**.) Now, if you decide to take the "2¢ option" on the contest, you'll be *doubling* your money for 21 days, and you want to watch it grow. To do this, Press:
× 2 = .

Now another "little jewel" — right above the key labelled $\boxed{\text{SST}}$ you'll see the word "Pause" written on the face of the machine. Whenever a word or function is printed above a key — on the face of the machine instead of right on the key — that's called a "second function".

Second functions allow us to pack all the power we can into your calculator, without loading it with keys. To use a second function, just push the $\boxed{\text{2nd}}$ key — in the upper left hand corner, and *then* the key right below the second function. In this book, we will use keys with a black background ■■ to indicate second functions. So:
    PRESS: $\boxed{\text{2nd}}$ $\boxed{\text{Pause}}$ (You'll press $\boxed{\text{2nd}}$ and the key labelled "SST".)

The $\boxed{\text{Pause}}$ key tells your machine:
"Stop for a moment and let's see what's going on".

One more thing — we want to *keep* doubling our money again and again. To let your machine know this, just find the $\boxed{\text{RST}}$ (reset) key (close to the lower left corner). This key says, "go back and do it again, from the top". PRESS: $\boxed{\text{RST}}$

You have taught your machine all it needs to know at this point, so press $\boxed{\text{LRN}}$ again, and press $\boxed{\text{RST}}$ again to be sure everything is back at the beginning.

Now, to watch your 2¢ "grow" — first:
Enter 2¢ on your calculator: PRESS $\boxed{\cdot}$ $\boxed{0}$ $\boxed{2}$ (The display should read **0.02**.)

At this point, your calculator is ready to "grow your money" — each display readout will be double the value before it. You'll start things going and count the days as they go by. You'll have 0.04 for the first day, etc. When you reach 21 days, the cash value in the display is what you will win.

O.K. — to start the machine, just press the RUN/STOP key — $\boxed{\text{R/S}}$ — the lower left key on the board. Keep your eye on the display, count out 21 days, then press the $\boxed{\text{R/S}}$ key again and hold it down for a moment.

On day 21 you'll have won $41,943.04! Tell the announcer you'll take the "2¢ option".

Congratulations!

In this little example, you have already covered many of the key points
that make your programmable calculator easy and fun to use:

- The [LRN] key lets you "teach the calculator". (You can teach it up to
  50 steps, and there is a lot it can learn — any of those "steps" is
  usually equivalent to any keystroke, but some steps can
  involve two or more keystrokes.)
- The [RST] key starts things back at the beginning.
- The [R/S] key allows you to control the action — stopping and
  starting where you please.

Making Tracks

One way of looking at how the calculator works is to think of it as a little
"railroad" — where you can "make tracks" for the machine to follow:

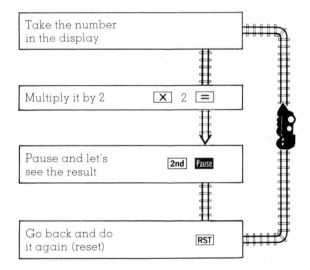

The "train" on this track has a special name — the "Pointer" (or, more
technically, the program pointer). Each time this train passes an
operation, the calculator follows the instruction or performs the operation
listed. The calculator in effect *pushes its own buttons* for you — in the
exact sequence you tell it. When you push the [RST] key (or the train comes
to [RST] as part of a program), the train immediately goes back to the
beginning — to the first step (step number 00), and starts over. To get the
"train" moving, or to stop it once it's moving, you just use the [R/S]
("run/stop") key.

In the example you considered earlier, when you press R/S, the machine simply pressed its own buttons and doubled the display value:

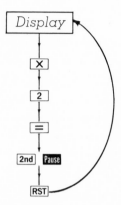

and would have kept on doing this for quite awhile — had you not stopped things after 21 "go-rounds" with the R/S key. (As you'll see later on, these repetitive "go-round" situations in your calculator — and in larger computers — are called "loops".)

At this point you're already well into many of the features that make your programmable calculator so special. Actually, we've explained enough here so that you can now explore all sorts of programs on your own. We'll naturally show you all the ins and outs of your machine with more on how to solve problems and run programs using it, later in the manual. But don't be afraid to explore. There's really nothing to it, and you can't hurt the calculator by pressing any combination of buttons. Your calculator can be easily programmed to run through any set of keystrokes (up to 50 steps) which you could handle manually from the keyboard.

Just: Push LRN
- Enter your keystrokes
  (You'll need to use RST as your last step if you want things to repeat, or R/S as your last step if you want things to stop after one time. Also, if you need to enter a number midway in a program, or want to see some intermediate result, just put an R/S at that point.)
- Press LRN again
- Press RST
  At this point you've programmed your calculator. To run the program, just:
- Enter the number(s) you want to work on
- Press R/S

A PRACTICAL CASE

We'll be showing you many ways to use your programmable calculator for a variety of school, home and recreational applications. You'll see with each example the ease and power the machine can bring to everyday mathematics. Let's take a quick look at a more practical case.

In this situation let's say that you (or someone you know) ran up a rather large bill (say $500) on a credit card account. Credit cards are convenient, but they really "sock you" with interest charges — typically 1.5% per month. You'd like to weigh several alternatives on payments and get a picture as to what the best course of action would be. Paying back the cash right away would be the best way, of course, but you might not be able to afford it. However, if you string the payments out over a long period, it would cost quite a bit.

Your calculator can help by speedily letting you calculate the alternatives.

For right now, let's say you'd like to know what your monthly payments would be if you paid off in 3, 6, 9, or 12 months, and how much you'd be paying in interest in each case.

HERE'S ALL YOU DO:

First, turn your calculator off and on — to clear everything — and then push the following keys. (Remember, we'll be covering all the details later — for now just see what your calculator will do for you! Push each key carefully.)

LRN
RCL 1 ×
(RCL 2 ÷
(1 − (1 + RCL 2)
yˣ RCL 3 +/−)) =
R/S
× RCL 3 =
− RCL 1 =
R/S (At this point your display should read **27 00**. If it doesn't, turn your calculator OFF and ON, and go back and re-key carefully.)

Now press:
LRN

At this point, all you need to do is store the values you want to try out in the three memories we've used, and let your calculator do the rest.

Enter the amount you owe and store it in memory one by pressing:

500 [STO] **1**

Enter your monthly interest rate (i = 1.5% = .015) and store it in memory two.

.015 [STO] **2**

Enter the first option you'd like to try — equal payments for n = 3 months:

3 [STO] **3**

From now on in it's a cinch!
First press [2nd] [fix] **2** so we'll be reading out dollars and cents clearly in the calculator's display.
Then press [RST] [R/S].

There it is: If you decided to pay back in 3 months, your monthly payment would be — $171.69.

Press [R/S] again to see how much you'd be charged for interest — $15.07.

To try the other options:
Enter 6 months, press 6 [STO] **3**
Then press [RST] [R/S]
Your payment: $87.76
Press [R/S] again for interest charges: $26.58

Enter 9 months, press 9 [STO] **3**
Then press [RST] [R/S]
Your payment: $59.80
Press [R/S] again for interest charges: $38.24

Enter 12 months, press 12 [STO] **3**
Then press [RST] [R/S]
Your payment: $45.84
Press [R/S] again for interest charges: $50.08

You can now go on and pick a payment program very carefully, seeing exactly how much your interest charge will be for each alternative.

In this example you've used your calculator to handle a very important and versatile business formula. The formula for calculating the amount of (equal monthly) payments on a credit card type of account is:

$$\text{Payment} = \text{PV} \times \left(\frac{i}{1 - (1 + i)^{-n}} \right)$$

Where: i = the *monthly* interest rate (1.5% or .015)
n = number of months
PV = the *present value* of the balance you owe ($500)

The *total interest charge* in dollars is calculated as:
Total Interest Charge = (n × payment) − PV
In handling the problem above the present value of the balance owed (PV) was stored in memory 1.
The monthly interest rate (i%) was stored in memory 2, and the number of months you take (n) was stored in memory 3.

From now on in you can "try out" any number of months you'd like (for any present value, or any interest rate) just by changing what you've got stored in one of the three memories. Your calculator does all the work at the touch of a key.

MOVING ON

Well, at this point you've already come quite a long way. You've seen your calculator in action in two program situations — each of which has a useful side as well as a fun side. What we hope is that you've also seen how easy it is to use and program your calculator. Let's make a few major points about your machine before we move on:

First of all, your programmable calculator is versatile and powerful — and you can do all sorts of manual calculations right off the keyboard anytime.

Secondly, your calculator is programmable — and all this really means is that it can remember keystroke instructions you give it, then go back and push its own buttons for you. We've seen that programming the machine to follow instructions is quite easy.

- Just push LRN
- Enter your keystroke instructions
- Push LRN again
- Push RST (don't forget this one — your program needs to start at the right place, and RST starts it back at the first step)
- From then on in, you just enter numbers you want to work on and press R/S

This new dimension of programmability brings several special benefits to you. Faster and more accurate calculations — particularly in repetitive situations — are now possible. You'll find it easier to use your calculator as part of decision-making processes, in exploring relationships in math, and in a host of everyday life and career applications.

Thirdly, and probably most important, your programmable calculator should be a lot of fun to use! Don't be afraid to explore with it.

ABOUT THE REST OF THIS BOOK

In this chapter our aim was to whet your appetite — to get you involved with and using your calculator right away. The following chapters were designed to allow you to learn about the machine at your own pace, depending on how much you know about calculators and programming.

Chapter 2 —Firing Up is a guided tour of all the keys of your calculator, except those specifically designed to program the machine. As we mentioned earlier, your programmable calculator is a versatile, general purpose machine — apart from its programmability. (If you're already familiar with advanced calculators that are not programmable, you may want to skip right on to the chapters on programming.)

Chapters 3,4, 5 & 6 introduce the world of programming. In these sections, through a series of step-by-step examples, we'll introduce you to the programming features of your calculator, as well as to the easy and fun side of programming itself. (If you are an experienced programmer and just need to learn more about how to program your calculator specifically, you may want to skip right on to *Chapter 7*.)

Chapter 7 —The Trackmakers is a key-by-key review of the programming keys and features of your calculator, with detailed descriptions.

The subsequent chapters of "Making Tracks" are devoted to a wide variety of example situations, case histories, and pre-written programs you can use in everyday life problem solving, or to just learn more about the machine. Operational details, battery and power considerations, what to do in case of trouble, etc., are covered in the appendices.

So depending on where you are in learning about calculators and programming, you can pick a path through this book that's quickest and best for you. For any user, however, we'd recommend that you read through this manual completely to avoid missing anything.

So enjoy your machine! It's a powerful bundle of technology you can hold in your hand and explore with. You may find that, with it as a tool and guide, a whole new side of the world of numbers and math can be opened for you.

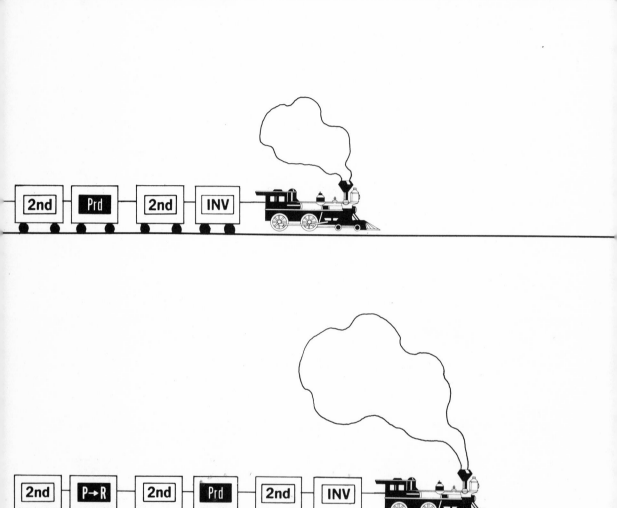

A TOUR OF KEYS AND FUNCTIONS

Your calculator is a powerful problem-solving device that's especially designed for easy use. You've already seen some simple programs in action, and we'll continue to discuss the programming side of your calculator's capability in later chapters. But apart from its programmability — your calculator is a versatile and powerful "slide rule" calculator. It's always ready to handle calculations right from the keyboard. In this chapter we'll be touring the direct problem-solving keys on your machine — the keys you can use immediately to get answers. Then, in later chapters, we'll show you how these basic keys can be used with the others on the keyboard to create programs.

The keyboard of your calculator has been organized and arranged in a common sense, straightforward way.

You can easily do simple things like balancing your checkbook or adding your grocery bill, as well as complex technical problems. The usefulness of any machine or tool, however, depends on the person who operates it. You'll want to get familiar with *all* of its features — all of what it will (and will not) do for you.

To get full use from your calculator, take the few minutes necessary just to see each key in action!

To make it easy for you to get acquainted, this tour is divided into three major sections:
> *Basic Keys and Functions*
> *Advanced/"Slide Rule" Keys and Functions*
> *Statistical Functions and Keys*

For those of you who have already owned or are familiar with an advanced slide rule calculator — you may want to skip to *Chapter 3* and get right into programming. If there are some keys on the machine you don't know about, however, we'd advise that you take this quick tour. Take out your calculator and keep it handy as we go through the keys — relax — and let's go.

SECTION 1: BASIC KEYS AND FUNCTIONS

We'll begin with a brief look at the basic "chassis" of your calculator, before we go on to check out the "extra options". These basics are what allow you to get information into and out of the machine — and let you handle the arithmetic part of mathematics quickly and accurately.

THE DISPLAY

Whenever you first turn on your calculator, you should see a single zero in the display indicating that all is well, the machine's on, and it's ready for action. Just turning the calculator OFF and ON clears everything inside. To check out your calculator's display, press the 8 key, the decimal point key ⟨·⟩, the change sign key ⟨+/−⟩, and then push the 8 key until the whole display is lit up. You can enter up to 8 digits into your calculator at any one time, for both positive and negative numbers. (Entries after the 8th digit are ignored.) For extra accuracy, however, results of calculations are computed to eleven digits inside your calculator, and then rounded off to 8 digits in the display. Notice that the negative sign stays immediately to the left of any negative number in the display, for easy reading.

To continue the tour, press the clear key ⟨CLR⟩ in the upper right corner of keyboard, and read on.

2nd AND INV : THE "DUAL FUNCTION" KEYS

Your calculator is loaded with functions to make all sorts of calculations easy and accurate. To allow you access to all of this power, without loading the machine with keys, many of the calculator keys have more than one function. The first function of the key is printed right on it. To use the first function on any key — just press it. The second function of a key is printed right above it. To use second functions, just press the 2nd key (upper left on the keyboard), and then the key right below the function you wish to use. (We'll indicate second functions in this book with a black background key ■ . For example, to put a π in the display you'll use the key sequence 2nd π .)

The inverse key — INV — also provides additional calculator functions without increasing the number of keys on the keyboard. The INV key "reverses" the purpose or function of certain keys. *Note:* In cases where you need to use both the 2nd and INV keys — you can use them in either order and get the same result. If you use the INV before a function with no inverse, it's simply ignored.

CLEARING THE CALCULATOR

There are several procedures that allow you to clear various parts of your calculator, or to clear the entire machine — depending on your needs as you proceed through a problem.

CE The [CE] (clear entry) key clears the last number you entered into the calculator, as long as that number wasn't followed by a function or operation key. (So if you accidentally hit a [5] instead of a [6] in the middle of an entry, just hit [CE] and try again.) This key will also stop the display from flashing if you've created an error condition in your calculator (we'll say more about this later). The [CE] key, however, doesn't affect pending operations, what's stored in the memories, or calculated results.

CLR —The [CLR] (clear) key (upper right on your machine) essentially clears the entire machine, *except* for data stored in the memories, settings made on the display format, and program steps.

2nd **C.t** — This allows you to clear only the "t" register (or "t" memory). This capability is beneficial in programming and with statistical functions. We'll look at it in more detail later.

INV **2nd** **C.t** — This key sequence clears everything in the machine except program steps and decimal settings. (Technically, this doesn't clear the first two registers of the math stack, but this will seldom be a problem.)

OFF-ON — Turning the calculator OFF, then ON again clears everything.
In fact, it's one sure way to quickly clear all your program steps, memories, display setting . . . everything!

---

[0] - [9] [•] [+/−] — DATA ENTRY KEYS

Your calculator operates with a full floating decimal point, and numbers
are entered into the machine with the data entry keys [0] - [9] [•] [+/−].
As you enter any number, the decimal point stays to the right of your
entry until the decimal point key ([•]) is pressed. After pressing the
decimal key, the fractional part of the number is keyed in, and the
decimal point floats to the left with it. To change the sign of a number in
the display, just push the change sign key [+/−] once. (Pressing [+/−] again
changes the sign back again.)

[+] [−] [X] [÷] AND [=] — BASIC OPERATION KEYS

Basic arithmetic is handled with the 5 basic operation keys: [+] [−] [X]
[÷] and [=]. Your calculator is equipped with a simple and powerful
entry system — the AOS™ entry method. This entry system makes problem
solution exceptionally easy. You just key in the problem the way it's
written, press [=], and get your result. The amazing feature of the AOS
system is that it automatically sorts out mixed operations in a problem for
you, and applies them in the correct order as it calculates your result.
(We'll say more about the AOS entry system in the next section.)

When you press the [=] key, all pending operations (things waiting to
happen inside your calculator) are completed. You get your result, and
the calculator is cleared — ready to start on the next problem.

Example: Calculate $15 + 7 \times 31 - 4 = ?$

PRESS	DISPLAY/COMMENTS
15 [+] 7 [X] 31	
[−] 4 [=]	**228.**

Note: The AOS system of entry makes it easy to get the right answer in
this example, and not all calculators have it.

THE AOS™ ENTRY METHOD

Mathematics is a science which adheres to a variety of rules. One such
rule is that it never permits two different answers to the same series of
operations. Because of this requirement — one solution for any
computation — mathematicians have established a set of universally
accepted rules when mixed operations are used in one calculation. For
example, the problem:

$$3 + 10 - 2 \times 14 \div 7 = ?$$

has *only one right answer!* (Know what it is? It's 9.)

You can key this problem directly, left to right, into your calculator
equipped with the AOS entry system and you'll get the correct answer.
The calculator sorts the operations you enter, applies them in the correct
order, and lets you see what it's doing along the way. Your calculator's
AOS entry system is quite an organizer! It sorts and then performs
operations it receives from you in the following universally accepted order:

1) Special Single Variable function keys (x^2 $\sqrt{x}$ etc.) — act on the
    displayed number immediately — as soon as you push the key. (We'll
    talk more about each of these keys later in the "tour" — but they
    include all the keys for the trig and log functions and their inverses,
    as well as square root, and reciprocal keys.)

2) Exponential calculations y^x and INV y^x (or $\sqrt[x]{y}$) are done next
    (we'll discuss these further in a following section).

3) Multiplications and divisions are completed next, in order from left to
    right, followed by

4) Additions and subtractions, in order from left to right.

Finally, the equals key $=$ completes all operations.

When you were in elementary school you may have heard the memory
aid "My Dear Aunt Sally" (MDAS) applied to help you remember the
last part of this hierarchy: Multiplications and Divisions first, in order left
to right — then Additions and Subtractions in the same way. In a
calculator equipped with the AOS entry system — all of this is
remembered for you.

There are cases in problem-solving where *you* may want to exactly
specify the order in which an expression is evaluated, or the way in
which a problem is completed. In these cases you can control the order
with the parentheses keys $($ $)$ discussed in the next section.
Parentheses demand a special first level of attention in mathematics —
and they're treated that way by your calculator.

(( )) – PARENTHESES KEYS

In a variety of problems you may need to specify the exact order in which expressions are evaluated, or the way in which numbers are grouped, as a problem is solved. Parentheses give you a way to "cluster" numbers and operations. By putting a series of numbers and operations in parentheses you tell the calculator: "Evaluate this little problem first — down to a single number result, then use this result for the rest of the calculation." *Within* each set of parentheses your calculator will operate according to the rules of algebraic hierarchy. You should use parentheses if you have any doubts in your mind about how the calculator will handle an expression.

There is a limit to the number of parentheses that can be opened at one time, and how many "pending" operations can be handled. Your calculator allows you to open nine parentheses at one time, with up to four operations pending — exceeding these limits results in a flashing display. (You'll rarely encounter this as a problem.)

Note an important point when using parentheses. You may often see equations or expressions written with parentheses to indicate implied multiplication: $(2 + 1)(3 + 2) = 15$. Your calculator will *not* recognize implied multiplications. You must key in the operation between the parentheses:

(2 + 1) × (3 + 2) = 15.

Here's an example on using parentheses:

Evaluate $\dfrac{(8 \times 4) + (9 \times -19)}{(3 + 10 \div 7) \times 2} =$

Solution: In problems of this type — you want the calculator to evaluate the entire numerator, then divide by the entire denominator. You can be sure of this taking place by placing an extra set of parentheses around the numerator and denominator as you key the problem in.

PRESS	DISPLAY/COMMENTS
((8 × 4) +	**32.** (8x4) displayed
(9 × 19 +/-)	
) ÷	**– 139.** The value of the numerator
((3 + 10 ÷ 7	
) × 2)	**8.8571429** Value of denominator
=	**– 15.693548** The final result.

MEMORY KEYS

There are 8 multi-purpose memories available for you to use in your calculator. These memories are special locations in the machine where you can store numbers you may need to use later on. The memories are a real bonus — and in many ways give you "several calculators" in one, since you can store, recall or perform arithmetic on the numbers in the memories without affecting calculations you have in progress in the "main machine".

The [CE] and [CLR] keys will not affect what's in the memories — but you can use the [INV] [2nd] [C.t] key sequence to clear them all out if you need to. (Turning the calculator OFF and ON does this, too.)

Since the calculator has 8 memories, you need to tell it which one you want to work with at any given time. Every time you push a memory key you need to follow it immediately with the number of the memory you are using ($n = $ **0, 1, 2, 3, 4, 5, 6,** or **7**). This tells the machine which one of the 8 memories you're referring to at the moment. The operations of the memory keys are pretty much "common sense" as shown below.

[STO] n — THE STORE KEY

This key just "stores" the displayed number in the memory you specify with **n** (**n** = **0, 1, 2, . . . 7**). (Any number previously stored in memory **n** is automatically cleared out first.)

[RCL] n — THE RECALL KEY

Any time you press [RCL] **n**, the number stored in memory **n** appears in the display and can be used in operations and calculations. The number remains in the memory after you press [RCL] **n**, and you can recall the value from any memory as many times as you need to in any calculation. A stored number remains in memory until you alter it with another memory operation, the [INV] [2nd] [C.t] clearing operation, or by turning the calculator off.

An example of the use of the memories:

Let's say that:
$a = 10.3 \, (25 - 1.7)$
$b = 15a + 6$
$c = 20b$, and you need to find c.

PRESS	DISPLAY/COMMENTS
10.3 ☒ ⬚ 25 ⊟	Calculate and store a
1.7 ⬚ ⊟	**239.99**
STO 1	**239.99** a stored in memory 1
15 ☒ RCL 1 ⊞ 6 ⊟	**3605.85**
STO 2	**3605.85** b stored in memory 2
20 ☒ RCL 2 ⊟	**72117.** The value of c.

MEMORY ARITHMETIC

In addition to the basic memory keys, there are a series of keys that let you perform arithmetic on the numbers stored in memory without affecting other calculations in progress:

SUM **n** — The Sum Key — allows you to algebraically add whatever number is in the display directly to the number stored in any memory. (This doesn't affect any calculations in progress.) The result of the addition stays stored in the memory. *Note:* This process is different from what happens when you use the STO key. The STO **n** operation clears out the number in the memory, and replaces it with the number in the display. (The display is not affected by this operation.)

INV SUM **n** — The Subtract key sequence, subtracts the number in the display from the number in memory **n**. The result stays stored in memory **n**. (The display does not change.)

2nd Prd **n** — The "Multiply" or Product key sequence, multiplies the number in memory **n** by what's in the display. The product stays stored in memory **n**. (The display does not change.)

INV 2nd Prd **n** — The "Divide" or Quotient key sequence, divides the number in memory **n** by the number in the display. The quotient stays stored in memory **n**. (Note the INV and 2nd may be pressed in either order for this sequence: 2nd INV Prd **n** for any "memory divide" calculation.) The display does not change during this operation.

2nd Exc **n** — The Exchange key sequence just "swaps" the number in memory **n** with the number in the display. (The display value gets stored in memory **n**, while the number stored in memory **n** is displayed.)

$\boxed{x \colon t}$ — The "x" Exchange with "t" Key

This is a special exchange key that exchanges the number in the display with the number in memory **7**. Memory **7** is used in several special functions on your machine and is given a special name: the "t" or "test" register. The $\boxed{x \colon t}$ key is identical in function to the $\boxed{2nd}$ $\boxed{Exc}$ **7** key sequence.

Additional Notes on Memories:

The 8 memories in your machine are designed primarily for your use and convenience — but there are times (particularly in more complex calculations) where your machine needs extra "space" to work in. In these cases your calculator will need to use the memories, and this can affect numbers you have stored in them. We'll mention these cases here — and review them again as various special machine features are discussed.

- When you're evaluating a complex expression, involving 3 or 4 levels of pending operations, memories **5** and **6** will be used.

- Memory **7**, the t register, will be used whenever the $\boxed{x \colon t}$ key is used.

- Statistical functions and trend line analysis problems (discussed later) may use memories **0, 1, 2, 3, 4, 5** and **7.**

- The $\boxed{2nd}$ $\boxed{Dsz}$ key sequence, which is discussed in *Chapter 4*, (and later chapters), works with memory zero.

In practice these memory situations aren't often a problem — but if you're really "loading up" the machine with work to do, you need to be aware of the fact that some of what you may have stored in memories can be affected.

SECTION 2: ADVANCED/ "SLIDE RULE" KEYS

In this section we move on to discuss some of the features of your calculator that are especially helpful in engineering, scientific, and more advanced mathematical applications (applications that not too long ago used to be handled with mechanical slide rules and tables). Many of these features have only been made possible by more recent developments in Integrated Circuit (IC) Technology. These new developments allow calculator designers to "put" various functions and tables right into the IC chip. This way you can put the calculator to work on a complex calculation with the touch of a key.

EE – SCIENTIFIC NOTATION KEY

In many applications, particularly in science and engineering, you may need to calculate with extremely large or small numbers. Such numbers are easily handled (by both you and your calculator) using scientific notation. A number in scientific notation is expressed as a base number (or "mantissa") times ten raised to some power (or "exponent").

$$\text{Mantissa} \times 10^{\text{power}}$$

To enter a number in scientific notation
- Enter the mantissa (then press +/− if it's negative.)
- Press EE (Enter Exponent) — a "00" will appear at the right of the display.
- Enter the power of 10 (then press +/− if it's negative.)

A number such as $-3.8901448 \times 10^{-32}$ will look like this in your display:

In scientific notation the power of ten (the two digits to the right in your display) tells you where the decimal point would have to be if you were writing the number out in longhand. A positive exponent tells you how many places the decimal point should be shifted to the right, a negative exponent — how many places to the left. For example:
2.9979×10^{8} equals 2.99790000
(Move decimal 8 places right, add zeroes as needed.)

1.6021×10^{-19} equals $.000\ 000\ 000\ 000\ 000\ 000\ 1.6021$ (Move decimal 19 places left, add zeroes as needed.)

Note: The key sequence EE INV EE will truncate the "guard digits" of a result leaving only the rounded display for further use. See Appendix D.

2nd Fix n — Fix Decimal Control

This very convenient feature allows you to choose the number of digits
you'd like to have displayed to the right of the decimal point as you go
through your calculations. Just press 2nd Fix then press the desired
number of decimal places (0 to 7). Try it — press 2nd Fix 3 — the display
immediately changes to "0.000".

The calculator will round all of your subsequent results to this number of
decimal places. You can go on and make number entries with as many
digits as you like, and the calculator will retain its own internal (11-digit)
accuracy. The display value will continue to be correctly rounded to the
number of decimal places you've selected. Note also that you can use the
fix key to set the desired number of decimal places whether you're in
standard display format or scientific notation. Turning your calculator
OFF and ON again erases the "fix" condition. Try the following example.

Example: ⅔ = 0.6666667

PRESS	DISPLAY/COMMENTS	
OFF-ON	**0**	
CLR	**0**	
2 ÷ 3 =	**0.6666667**	
2nd Fix 6	**0.666667**	*(Note:* display
2nd Fix 2	**0.67**	value is correctly
2nd Fix 1	**0.7**	rounded)
2nd Fix 0	**1.**	

To Clear The "Fix" Condition:

You can "unfix" your calculator's display with the following key
sequences:

INV 2nd Fix

2nd Fix 9

Turning the calculator OFF and ON (this clears everything).

2nd π — "Pi" Key Sequence

The 2nd π key sequence displays the first 8 digits of π. (Eleven digits are entered into the calculator — 8 correctly rounded digits are displayed.) The number you'll see displayed is: **3.1415927**. This key sequence displays π immediately, doesn't affect calculations in progress, and can be used anytime in a calculation.

2nd |x| — Absolute Value Key Sequence

When this key sequence is pressed, the sign of the number in the display (x) is made positive. This feature comes in handy in a variety of calculating (and programming) situations.

When 2nd |x| is pressed:
If the sign of the number in the display is negative, it's changed to positive.
If the sign of the number in the display is positive, things are left alone. This key can be used any time in a calculation, and doesn't affect calculations in progress.

Note that several keys on the keyboard use the letter "x" as part of their marking. The "x" on these keys just means "the number in the display".

x^2 $\sqrt{x}$ $1/x$ — Square, Square Root and Reciprocal Keys

These 3 easily accessible keys are essentials for speedily handling a variety of algebraic and equation solving situations. All three of these keys act immediately on the number in the display (x), and don't affect calculations in progress.

x^2 — The Square Key — calculates the square of the number in the display (multiplies the displayed number by itself).

$\sqrt{x}$ — Square Root Key — Calculates the square root of the number in the display. The square root of a number (say x) is another number (labelled $\sqrt{x}$), such that:
$$(\sqrt{x}) \times (\sqrt{x}) = x.$$

$1/x$ — The Reciprocal Key — Divides the displayed number into one.

$\boxed{y^x}$ — Universal Power Key

This powerful key allows you to raise a (positive) number to a power at the touch of a key. To use this key:

- Enter the number you want to raise to a power (y)
- Press $\boxed{y^x}$
- Enter the power (x)
- Press $\boxed{=}$ (or any operation key)

Example: Calculate $3.1897^{4.7343}$

Press	Display/Comments
$\boxed{\text{CLR}}$	**0** Clear
3.1897 $\boxed{y^x}$	**3.1897** "y" value
4.7343	**4.7343** "x" value
$\boxed{=}$	**242.60674** Final result: y^x

$\boxed{\text{INV}}$ $\boxed{y^x}$ — Universal Root Key Sequence ($\sqrt[x]{y}$)

This key sequence allows you to take roots of a positive number (the inverse of y^x, or the $\sqrt[x]{y}$). Before calculators came along, calculations like this were usually pretty time consuming — and involved a set of logarithm tables.) To use this key sequence to take $\sqrt[x]{y}$:

- Enter the number you want to take the root of (y)
- Press $\boxed{\text{INV}}$ $\boxed{y^x}$
- Enter the root you want to take (x)
- Press $\boxed{=}$ (or any operation key)

Example: Calculate $\sqrt[3.871]{21.496}$

Press	Display/Comments
$\boxed{\text{CLR}}$	**0** Clear
21.496 $\boxed{\text{INV}}$ $\boxed{y^x}$	**21.496** "y" value
3.871	**3.871** "x" value
$\boxed{=}$	**2.2089685** Final result ($\sqrt[x]{y}$).

Note: The $\boxed{y^x}$ key (and $\boxed{\text{INV}}$ $\boxed{y^x}$) key sequences perform calculations that involve quite a few steps inside your calculator, and it takes a little longer to complete these calculations than others. *Be sure you wait for your calculator to finish — with a final result in the display before pressing additional keys.*

$\boxed{\ln x}$ AND $\boxed{\text{2nd}}$ $\boxed{\text{log}}$ — LOGARITHM KEYS

Logarithms are mathematical functions that enter into a variety of technical and theoretical calculations. In addition, they form an important part of many mathematical "models" of natural phenomena. The logarithm keys give you immediate access to the "log" of any positive number (within calculator limits) — without having to hassle with bulky tables.

$\boxed{\ln x}$ — The Natural Logarithm Key — immediately displays the natural logarithms (base e = 2.7182818) of the number in the display. (*Note:* the number in the display must be positive — attempting to take $\boxed{\ln x}$ of a negative number will result in a flashing display.)

$\boxed{\text{2nd}}$ $\boxed{\text{log}}$ — The Common Logarithm Key — immediately displays the common logarithm (base 10) of the (positive) number in the display.

$\boxed{\text{INV}}$ $\boxed{\ln x}$ AND $\boxed{\text{INV}}$ $\boxed{\text{2nd}}$ $\boxed{\text{log}}$ — ANTI-LOGARITHM KEY SEQUENCES

These key sequences are the "inverse" or "anti" functions of the logarithms. ($e^{(\ln x)} = x$, and $10^{(\log x)} = x$.) These calculations arise in many technical situations and can be handled quickly with just a few keystrokes on your calculator.

$\boxed{\text{INV}}$ $\boxed{\ln x}$ — e^x Key Sequence — Raises e to the power of the number in the display (calculates the natural antilogarithm of the number in the display).

$\boxed{\text{INV}}$ $\boxed{\text{2nd}}$ $\boxed{\text{log}}$ — 10^x Key Sequence — Raises 10 to the power of the number in the display (calculates the common antilogarithm of the display value).

Notes on logarithm and "anti" logarithm keys:

Each of these keys acts immediately on the number in the display — and doesn't affect calculations in progress. Your calculator uses a variety of "routines" for arriving at these values. Certain limits are set by these routines — and exceeding them may result in an error indication - see the *Appendix C: Error Conditions*, for details.

Some examples: Calculate log 15.32, ln 203.451, $e^{-.69315}$, 10^{π}

PRESS	DISPLAY/COMMENTS
15.32 $\boxed{\text{2nd}}$ $\boxed{\text{log}}$	**1.1852588**
203.451 $\boxed{\ln x}$	**5.3154252**
.69315 $\boxed{+/-}$ $\boxed{\text{INV}}$ $\boxed{\ln x}$	**0.4999986**
$\boxed{\text{2nd}}$ $\boxed{\pi}$ $\boxed{\text{2nd}}$ $\boxed{\text{INV}}$ $\boxed{\text{log}}$	**1385.4557**

2nd Int — "INTEGER PART OF A NUMBER" KEY SEQUENCE

This key sequence displays the *integer part* of any number in the display. For example, if you enter the number 3.1117 into the display, and press the 2nd Int key sequence, the calculator "chops off" everything to the right of the decimal point and displays only the integer 3. (Try it!)

There are many situations in mathematics where you'll find yourself needing to deal with *just* the integer part of a number. In programming you'll find this key sequence very handy for handling these situations.

2nd INV Int —"FRACTIONAL PART OF A NUMBER" KEY SEQUENCE

There are some instances in math and programming where you need to deal only with the decimal part of a number, and need to isolate it. This key sequence displays the fractional or decimal part of any number in the display. So if you enter 3.1117, and press the 2nd INV Int key sequence, 0.1117 will be displayed.

The following diagram summarizes these two key sequences:

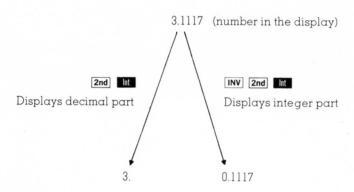

Note: The original number is lost when Int or INV Int is used — store it first if you'll need it later.

[2nd] Deg , [2nd] Rad , [2nd] Grad —ANGULAR MODE KEYS

Your calculator is equipped to handle a variety of calculations that
involve angles — notably the trigonometric functions and
polar/rectangular conversions. When performing these calculations,
your calculator allows you to select any one of three common units for
angular measure using the key sequences below:

[2nd] Deg — selects <u>degree</u> mode. In this mode all entered or calculated
angles are measured in degrees, until another mode is selected
(one degree equals $\frac{1}{360}$ of a circle — a right angle equals 90°).

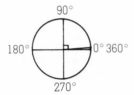

[2nd] Rad — selects <u>radian</u> mode. In this mode all angles are measured in
radians (one radian equals $\frac{1}{2\pi}$ of a circle; a right angle equals $\frac{\pi}{2}$ radians).

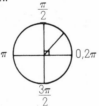

[2nd] Grad — selects <u>grad</u> mode. In this mode all angles are measured in
grads (one grad equals $\frac{1}{400}$ of a circle — a right angle equals 100 grads).

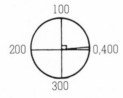

IMPORTANT NOTE: When you first turn your calculator on it powers up
in the degree mode, and stays in that mode until a new mode is
selected.

One very common error encountered when working with angles is finding
yourself in an incorrect angular mode. Once you select an angular
mode, your calculator will *stay in* that mode until you select a new one,
or until you turn the calculator OFF and ON again (the calculator is
always in degree mode on power up).

[2nd] [sin] , [2nd] [cos] , [2nd] [tan] — **TRIGONOMETRIC KEY SEQUENCES**

These key sequences immediately calculate the sine, cosine, and tangent of the angle in the display (angle is measured in units of selected angle mode). The trig functions relate the angles and sides of a right triangle as shown below:

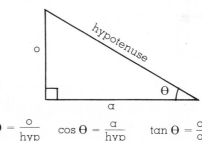

$$\sin \Theta = \frac{o}{hyp} \quad \cos \Theta = \frac{a}{hyp} \quad \tan \Theta = \frac{o}{a}$$

[INV] [2nd] [sin] , [INV] [2nd] [cos] , [INV] [2nd] [tan]

Using the [INV] preceding another key reverses the operation and intention of that key.

The [INV] [2nd] [sin] , [INV] [2nd] [cos] , and [INV] [2nd] [tan] key sequences calculate the *angle* (in the units of the mode selected), whose sine, cosine or tangent is in the display. (These key sequences calculate the arcsine ($\sin^{-1}$), arccosine ($\cos^{-1}$), and arctangent ($\tan^{-1}$), respectively.)

Examples: Calculate the sine of 90°, 90 radians, and 90 grads, and the arctan of 1.

PRESS	**DISPLAY/COMMENTS**
OFF-ON [CLR]	**0** Clear the entire machine (Powers up in degrees mode)
90 [2nd] [sin]	**1.** sin of 90 degrees
90 [2nd] [Rad] [2nd] [sin]	**0.8939967** sin of 90 radians
90 [2nd] [Grad] [2nd] [sin]	**0.9876883** sin of 90 grads
1 [2nd] [Deg] [INV] [2nd] [tan]	**45.** The angle (in degrees) whose tangent is one.

ANGLE CONVERSIONS

You may at times find it necessary to convert angular values from one unit system to another. While there are no special conversion keys on your calculator for this purpose, the key sequences to convert angular units in the first and fourth quadrants are pretty simple and can be used without affecting the memories or calculations in progress.

1) Be sure the calculator is in the correct angular mode and enter the angle to be converted.
2) Press `2nd` `sin`
3) Change calculator to desired angular mode.
4) Press `INV` `2nd` `sin`

Example: Express 50 degrees in radians.

PRESS	DISPLAY/COMMENTS
`2nd` `Deg`	**0**
50 `2nd` `sin`	**0.7660444**
`2nd` `Rad`	
`INV` `2nd` `sin`	**0.8726646** Radians

(The angular range of these conversions is limited to the first and fourth quadrants. For larger angles you may convert directly:

- number of degrees $\times \frac{100}{90}$ = number of grads
- number of degrees $\times \frac{\pi}{180}$ = number of radians
- number of grads $\times \frac{90}{100}$ = number of degrees
- number of grads $\times \frac{\pi}{200}$ = number of radians
- number of radians $\times \frac{180}{\pi}$ = number of degrees
- number of radians $\times \frac{200}{\pi}$ = number of grads

Conversions:

Your calculator is equipped with two keys that make it especially handy in conversion situations.

[2nd] [D.MS] — Degrees, Minutes, Seconds To Decimal Degrees Conversions
This key sequence converts an angle expressed in degrees minutes and seconds to decimal degrees. The [INV] [2nd] [D.MS] key sequence does just the opposite — converting *from* decimal degrees *to* degrees minutes and seconds. This conversion is handy if you have to do arithmetic with angles, or with time — expressed in hours minutes and seconds.

To enter and convert an angle, just follow the format shown on the [D.MS] key label:
- Enter the number of degrees
- Press the decimal point key, [·]
- Enter the number of minutes (2 digits — less than 60)
- Enter the number of seconds (2 digits — less than 60)
- Press [2nd] [D.MS]

The decimal equivalent of the angle (or time) is now displayed. The reverse conversion is easy to do also:
- Enter the angle (whole number and decimal part)
- Press [INV] [2nd] [D.MS]

The angle is now displayed as the number of degrees, followed by a decimal point, followed by the number of minutes and seconds.

Example: Convert 47°05'38" to decimal degrees and back to degrees minutes and seconds again.

Press	Display/Comments
47.0538 [2nd] [D.MS]	**47.093889** angle decimal equivalent
[INV] [2nd] [D.MS]	**47.0538** back to degrees, minutes, seconds

Note that you can also convert hours, minutes, and seconds to decimal form by the same technique.

Occasionally, when converting to the degree, minute, second format, minutes or seconds may indicate 60 due to rounding. This simply indicates to round up to the next highest degree (or minute for 60 seconds). For example convert ⅔ minute to degrees, minutes, seconds.

Press	Display/Comments
2 [÷] 3 [=] [INV] [2nd] [D.MS]	**0.396** This is 0°39'60" or 40 minutes.

2nd P→R — POLAR TO RECTANGULAR CONVERSIONS

This is a handy feature of your calculator that is particularly useful in science and engineering applications. Working with the x⇌t key — it's fast and easy to convert from polar to rectangular coordinates, or vice versa. Just follow the key sequences illustrated below:

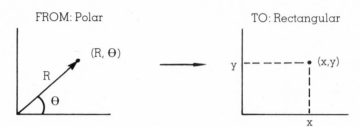

To convert *from* polar *to* rectangular coordinates:
- Enter your value for "R"
- Press x⇌t
- Enter your "θ" value (units selected with angular mode keys).
- Press 2nd P→R

"y" is now displayed; to read "x":
- Press x⇌t

"x" is now displayed.

To convert *from* rectangular *to* polar coordinates follow the sequence listed below:

- Enter your "x" value
- Press x⇌t
- Enter your "y" value
- Press INV 2nd P→R

"θ" is now displayed (in units selected by mode key); to read "R":
- Press x⇌t

"R" is now displayed.

Example: Convert R = 45 meters, θ = 31.6° into rectangular coordinates

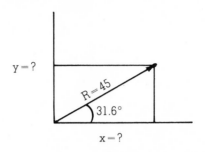

PRESS

Turn calculator OFF & ON
45 [x⇄t] 31.6
[2nd] [P→R]
[x⇄t]

DISPLAY/COMMENTS

0   Calculator is in degree mode
      Enter polar coordinates: R, then θ.
23.579366   "y" value
38.327712   "x" value

Note: This conversion will make use of memory 7 (the "t" register) — so be sure *not* to use memory 7 while you're doing a polar to rectangular conversion (you'll lose numbers stored there).

SECTION 3: STATISTICAL FUNCTIONS AND KEYS

In many situations — in school work, everyday life, or business, you may find yourself handling large sets of data points. This data could be from laboratory measurements, test scores, results from a study or research project, etc.

Your calculator is equipped with features allowing you to easily collect and analyze data by rapidly calculating mean, variance, and standard deviation. Intermediate results are stored in the memories for you in an easy to access fashion. (You'll find this especially useful in programming with statistics — as you'll see later on in this book.) You can also simultaneously analyze *two* sets of data, allowing you to examine relationships between them in advanced statistical programming.

To collect and analyze sets of data here's the procedure:
• Begin any and all statistical calculations by either turning your calculator OFF and ON, or by pressing the [INV] [2nd] **C.t** key sequence.

If you have only one set of data to analyze:
- Enter each data point
- Press [2nd] [Σ+]
- Repeat for all data points

- Press [2nd] [x̄] to calculate the *mean* of the data
- Press [2nd] [σ2] to calculate the *variance* of the data (with N weighting).
- Press [2nd] [σ2] [√x̄] to calculate the standard deviation of the data (with N weighting).
  ("N weighting" means that the total number of data points is used in the calculation of the variance — this type of variance is called a population variance.)

If you have two sets of data to analyze simultaneously:
Call the two sets of data "x" (independent) and "y" (dependent) *arrays* of data.
- Enter an "x" data point
- Press [x⇄t]
- Enter a "y" data point
- Press [2nd] [Σ+]
- Repeat for all points

- Press [INV] [2nd] [x̄] to calculate the mean of the "x" data points.
- Press [2nd] [x̄] to calculate the mean of the "y" data points
- Press [INV] [2nd] [σ2] to calculate the variance of the "x" data points
- Press [2nd] [σ2] to calculate the variance of the "y" data points
- Press [INV] [2nd] [σ2] [√x̄] to calculate the standard deviation of the "x" data points.
- Press [2nd] [σ2] [√x̄] to calculate the standard deviation of the "y" data points.

While you're doing any statistical analysis calculation, the data is collected in the memories as follows:

	0	**n** (The number of data points)
memory	**1**	Σy
	2	Σy^2
	3	Σx
	4	Σx^2
	5	Σxy
	7	Last x value entered, *plus one.*

Note also that the formula used for the variance is.

$$\text{Variance} = \frac{\Sigma(x_i - \bar{x})^2}{N} \text{ or } \frac{\Sigma(y_i - \bar{y})^2}{N}$$

The symbol Σ just means "the sum of".

If you make a mistake entering any data point, you can remove the bad points by re-entering them as before, but pressing INV before 2nd Σ+ as you key it in.

Example: You're grading an exam, and the scores are in. You'd like to see how well the class has done. The scores are tabulated below:

96 65 81
85 76 86
57 98 75
78 100 72
81 70 80

PRESS	**DISPLAY/COMMENTS**
INV 2nd C.t	**0** Be sure to clear the entire machine
96 2nd Σ+	**1.** The calculator counts
85 2nd Σ+	**2.** your data points for you
continue for all points	.
	.
	.
72 2nd Σ+	**14.**
80 2nd Σ+	**15.**
2nd x̄	**80.** Class average
2nd σ2 √x	**11.564313** Standard deviation.

SOME SPECIAL NOTES ON STATISTICAL FUNCTIONS

Occasionally, when you're dealing with the analysis of 2 sets of related data, you'll need to "step up" the x variable by one, for each "y" variable you enter. (For example, for data collected by year — 1961, 1962, 1963, etc.). In this case you only need to enter the first x value, and your calculator will automatically increment x by one for each y value entered. This feature is useful in programming what are called "trend line analyses"— which folks into statistics know about. Also, the variance calculations above all use "N weighting" — which as folks who use statistics know, is suitable for analyzing *population* data. Statisticians use (N-1) weighting when analyzing *sample* data. To obtain (N-1) weighting in variance calculations, you can use the following key sequence after calculating the variance from the keyboard:

$$\boxed{\times}\ \boxed{\text{RCL}}\ 0\ \boxed{\div}\ \boxed{(}\ \boxed{\text{RCL}}\ 0\ \boxed{-}\ 1\ \boxed{=}\ .$$

This multiplies by $\dfrac{n}{n-1}$

(Note that the square root of the variance is the standard deviation.)

ONE WAY TRIPS
3

THE BASICS ON GETTING INTO PROGRAMMING

Anyone can understand programming — in fact, you follow "programs" of various sorts throughout your everyday life. Anytime you follow a plan to get somewhere or achieve some desired result, a program of some kind is involved. Unfortunately, for many of us the words "programming", "programmable", and even "calculator" and "computer" are often shrouded in mystery. The fact is that programmable devices are really pretty simple. And in reality what computers do is easy to understand — and also *important* to understand.

The Future

Devices like your programmable calculator are dedicated to cutting through any "bunk" or mysterious clouds about programming. In this chapter we'll introduce you to many of the basics of programming through a series of step-by-step real world examples. You'll be learning with the help of your calculator giving you instant feedback. And — you'll be learning important stuff. Because one *truth* about programmable devices is this — more and more of your life is getting involved with them. It's well that it should — programmable devices can save time and money in handling information and helping make decisions — all with increased accuracy. So the more you know about programming, the more you'll be "in the know" when you come in contact with programmable devices.

In the future you'll be seeing more and more "programmable" things — from microwave ovens to home computers. By learning about programming now — easily — on your programmable calculator, you'll find these devices of the future quite easy to handle. You'll also be in a good position to easily move on to handling some of the bigger computers and programmable devices in our world today. Some of the procedures change, but the principles are basically similar.

Let's Go

So take out your machine, and get into "Making Tracks." This chapter deals with what we'll call *One Way Trips* — simple, straight line programs. Later chapters will cover such topics as:
  • *Round Trips* — repetitive programs or "loops".
  • *Fixing Tracks* — editing, changing, and repairing programs and *documenting* them.
  • *Switch Tracks* — building decision-making into your programs, and some more advanced subjects.

The examples in each chapter are divided too, into bite-sized pieces that tell you where you are each step of the way. These "pieces" are each identified with a graphic symbol for you. In the following examples you'll be seeing a brief introduction, and the sections described here:

 DESTINATION: This will boil down to a clear statement *what you want the calculator to do for you*, once you finish programming it.

 PLANNING THE ROUTE: A discussion of the techniques we'll be using — focusing on *what's new* in each section.

 MAKING TRACKS: Setting up a "track diagram", or flow chart that describes your program.

 RUNNING IT: Anytime you write a program, it's important to be sure things are working correctly. One way to do this is to run through it with an example whose answer you *know*. In this section we'll give you trial examples — and what results to expect.

 NEW KEYS: In examples where new keys are introduced and used in a new way, we'll review their operation for you.

Note that not all examples will have all of these sections. We'll be using them only where needed as we go along. In addition, some examples will have a section labeled:

 THE NEXT STOP: In this section we'll be giving you suggestions on how to "go further" in your learning about programming. A quick example for you to try on your own may be included — with typical answers in *Appendix E.*

TRAVEL EXPENSES

ONE WAY TRIPS

As you've seen in the last chapter, your programmable calculator is a versatile and powerful machine — even apart from its programmability. You can handle all sorts of calculations — from simple around-the-house math, to advanced scientific calculations — right off the keyboard. As it turns out, the simplest programs you can write for your calculator are just those where you "teach" it a series of keystrokes you'd normally handle manually from the keyboard; and then have it "push its own buttons" to run through them again.

These programs, which we'll call "one way trips", actually let you arrange it so that the push of a single key triggers many powerful calculations. In situations where you need to do many calculations over and over again, this feature can mean much greater speed and accuracy. The important keys involved in one way trips are the ⟨LRN⟩ ⟨R/S⟩ and ⟨RST⟩ keys — as you'll be seeing in this section.

TRAVEL EXPENSES:

Imagine for a moment that you're all set to strike off on that cross country vacation — and that you have the time to plan on a few of those "side trips" you'd like to make as well. Even with all the time needed, chances are your budget may have some limits on it. In this case it's a lot easier to run out of cash on your calculator before you do on the road. Let's say that you've determined that it costs $0.06 per mile to operate your car — counting gas, oil and "incidentals". With this information, you could handle the plan for simple trips easily on your calculator. If you plan to go 15 miles, then the cost is just 15 miles x $0.06 per mile:

PRESS	DISPLAY/COMMENTS
15	**15** Number of miles
⟨×⟩ 0.06 ⟨=⟩	**0.9**—90¢ is the trip cost.

If you're planning for a big trip made up of a lot of little trips, you'd keep right on doing this. Enter mileage, multiply by 6¢, get result. Here's a case where a program can help — anytime you're faced with an "over and over again" calculation it's prime time for a program.

DESTINATION

You'd like to arrange it so that all you have to do is enter the trip mileage on your calculator, and then with a simple key sequence get your trip cost (mileage × 6¢ per mile).

PLANNING THE ROUTE

In cases like this all you need to do is use the **LRN** key to teach the calculator the same key sequence you'd use to do the problem by hand. The only addition you need to make is to include a **R/S** at the end of the keystrokes you'd normally use to handle the calculations manually.

MAKING TRACKS

Here we'll give you a picture of the tracks you're laying down for the machine. (For the time being, don't worry about what's in the display while you're programming the machine.)

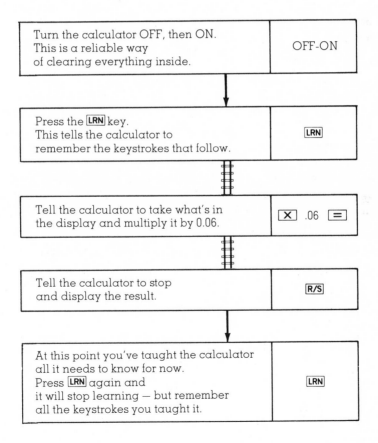

Turn the calculator OFF, then ON. This is a reliable way of clearing everything inside.	OFF-ON
Press the **LRN** key. This tells the calculator to remember the keystrokes that follow.	**LRN**
Tell the calculator to take what's in the display and multiply it by 0.06.	**×** .06 **=**
Tell the calculator to stop and display the result.	**R/S**
At this point you've taught the calculator all it needs to know for now. Press **LRN** again and it will stop learning — but remember all the keystrokes you taught it.	**LRN**

KEYING IN YOUR PROGRAM

Note that in most cases you can go ahead and key in your program right from the "flow" chart in the *Making Tracks* section. We'll just run through the steps again for you to be sure you've got them in correctly:

OFF-ON

LRN

✕ .06 =

R/S

LRN

In the *Making Tracks* section of each example, the flow diagrams are set up to tell you *why* you're entering each keystroke in a program:

RUNNING IT

You're all set to go at this point. To use your program for trip planning, just:

Enter the mileage.

Press RST (reset) — This starts your "train" — the program pointer — back at the beginning.

Press R/S (run/stop).

The RST and R/S keys are deliberately placed close to each other, one over the other, in the lower left on your keyboard. (In a few seconds we'll show you how to include RST as part of your programs — then it will take care of itself.) So if you're planning trips of 15.1, 35.6 and 231.4 miles just:

PRESS	DISPLAY/COMMENTS
15.1	**15.1** First mileage
RST R/S	**0.906** or 91¢ trip cost
35.6	**35.6** Mileage
RST R/S	**2.136** or $2.14 trip cost
231.4	**231.4** Mileage.
RST R/S	**13.884** or $13.88 trip cost

Try it for any trip mileage you'd like!

NEW KEYS

So we've seen that:

LRN — Is the "on/off' button for teaching your calculator. Press it once and you put your calculator in what might be called "learn" mode. The display changes to a new format: 00 00 which we'll discuss in more detail later. Once you've pressed LRN your calculator can be taught up to 50 steps. When you press LRN again, the calculator stops learning, but remembers all the program steps you taught it.

R/S — The run/stop key — does several things:
When written into a program, R/S tells the calculator to stop as soon as the program pointer comes to it.

Once you've finished teaching the program to your calculator and you've taken the calculator out of "learn" mode (by pressing LRN again), the R/S key starts up the program, or will stop it once it's running. (If the program is *stopped*, R/S *starts* it running. If it's *running*, R/S *stops* it.)

RST — The reset key, starts things back at the beginning. (If you forget to push this key, the program won't start in the right place and the program pointer may get "lost". A flashing display will result.)

NEXT STOP

Can you write a trip planning program similar to the one above, that will allow you to plan your trip in a rented car which costs $0.16 per mile?

Can you write a program that computes the sales tax (for your city, state, etc.) on any item whose price you enter into the display?

THE COMPLETE VACATION

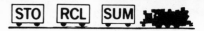

In this example, we'll take our trip planning situation a little further, and along the way show you a bit on how to use memories in your programs. In this case you'd like to be able to enter the mileage for various "legs" of your trip, get a look at the cost for that leg, and then the total you've spent up to that point. This way you can just go through a road atlas and plan your trip, with your calculator keeping constant tabs on total cost. Let's say the trip you'd like to take is made up of the segments shown in the map below:

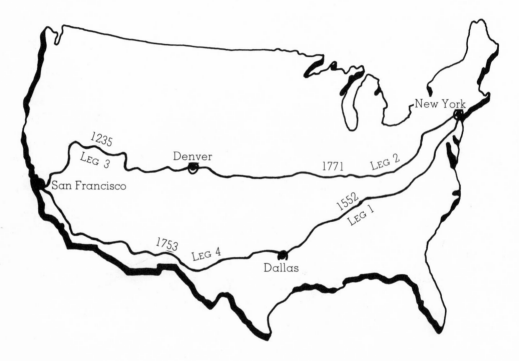

DESTINATION

You'd like to be able to enter the mileage for any leg of your trip, press R/S and see the cost for that leg, then press R/S again to see the total number of dollars you've spent to that point.

PLANNING THE ROUTE

You already know from our last example that to calculate the mileage cost for any leg of the trip, all you need to do is multiply the mileage by 0.06. We'll want to do this and then stop things for a look.

Then, to keep tabs on the *total trip mileage*, we'll need to accumulate the costs for each leg of the trip someplace. The perfect "place" for such things is one of the memories in your calculator. With the SUM key you can add the cost for each trip into a memory, then recall the running total with the RCL key any time you need it.

In case you've forgotten how the SUM key works, try this quick example. Add 5, 6, and 7 into memory 3, then recall the result:

PRESS	DISPLAY/COMMENTS
OFF-ON	**0** Clears everything
5 SUM 3	**5.** 5 summed into memory 3
6 SUM 3	**6.** 6 added into memory 3
7 SUM 3	**7.** 7 added into memory 3
RCL 3	**18.** The final sum collected in memory 3.

With the SUM key you can keep a running total in your program, and with a RCL and R/S you can get a look at that running total any time you'd like. Since money is involved, we'll also use a 2nd Fix 2-key sequence before we start the program, so our answers will always appear rounded to the nearest cent.

MAKING TRACKS

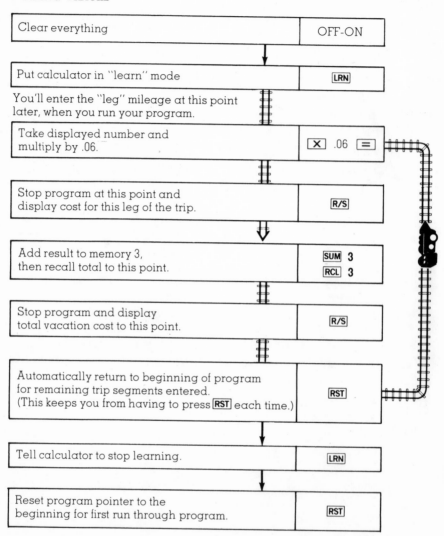

Clear everything	OFF-ON
Put calculator in "learn" mode	LRN

You'll enter the "leg" mileage at this point later, when you run your program.

Take displayed number and multiply by .06.	✕ .06 =
Stop program at this point and display cost for this leg of the trip.	R/S
Add result to memory 3, then recall total to this point.	SUM 3 RCL 3
Stop program and display total vacation cost to this point.	R/S
Automatically return to beginning of program for remaining trip segments entered. (This keeps you from having to press RST each time.)	RST
Tell calculator to stop learning.	LRN
Reset program pointer to the beginning for first run through program.	RST

You can key your program in, right from the flow chart, *after* you turn your calculator OFF and ON. (This important step clears the *entire* machine and will prevent left over keystrokes from previous examples causing any trouble in this one.)

Running It

Let's say the segments of the trip you've planned are as follows:

Dallas–New York, 1552 mi.
New York–Denver, 1771 mi.
Denver–San Francisco, 1235 mi.
San Francisco–Dallas, 1753 mi.

Note: Be sure your program is carefully entered from the flow chart on the previous page, then just enter the mileage for each leg and proceed:

Press	Display/Comments
[2nd] [Fix] 2	**0.00** This sets the display to read out dollars and cents, rounded to 2 decimal places
1552 [R/S]	**93.12** Cost of first leg
[R/S]	**93.12** Cost so far
1771 [R/S]	**106.26** Cost of second leg
[R/S]	**199.38** Total cost to Denver
1235 [R/S]	**74.10** Cost of third leg
[R/S]	**273.48** Total cost to San Francisco
1753 [R/S]	**105.18** Cost of 4th Leg
[R/S]	**378.66** Total trip cost

Note that if you'd like to try another trip with different cities, be sure to place a zero in memory 3 so you don't just keep adding costs onto the costs for this trip (just press 0 [STO] **3**).

New Keys

In this example we've seen how using memories as part of programs is easy to do, and we'll be seeing more on that in later examples. We've also seen how [RST] can be put right into the program, so you don't have to push it each time. Check back at our flow chart for a moment. In this case after the second [R/S] in your program, the program pointer (the "train" on your track that tells your calculator which keys to push) is waiting right before an [RST] instruction. When you enter a new mileage and press [R/S], the pointer goes down and hits [RST], which immediately starts things right back at the beginning for you.

Next Stop

Let's say your car is leaking oil. Write a program that lets you plan a trip in the same way as above, but that adds $5.00 in "extra" expense for each leg of the trip to cover buying a supply of oil at each major city.

ON SALE!

In this case let's say you've got a job in a department store. The manager thinks that running sales is a good idea. In fact, he has his employees marking down price tags throughout the store quite often. He also likes to vary the amount of the discount from department to department, 25% for shoes, 15% in hardware, etc. In this programming situation we'll review some of what you've seen in the first example and expand on using memories as part of programs.

DESTINATION

You'd like to be able to go to any department in the store that you're assigned, key in the price of any item on the shelf, press R/S and get the discounted price. You'd also like to be able to vary the amount of the discount as easily as your manager changes the discount amount from department to department.

PLANNING THE ROUTE

When an item is discounted by 25%, you can find the new price using the formula: "New price" = old price × (1-.25). In fact, for any discount amount you can find the new price from this same formula:

New price = old price × (1 – discount)

In our program, we'll store the discount amount as a decimal number (25% = 0.25) in memory 3. Then we'll recall it as we need to in calculating the new price.

New price = old price × (1- RCL 3).

The advantage of doing this in your program is that if you go to a new department with a new discount rate, all you'll need to do is store the new rate in memory 3, then proceed. This technique is a handy one in many situations where you'd like to change a number in a program without rewriting the program itself.

Making Tracks

Clear the entire machine, and tell it to get ready to learn.	OFF-ON [LRN]
Take what's in the display and discount it using our formula.	[×] [(] 1 [−] [RCL] 3 [)] [=]
Stop and display the result.	[R/S]
Automatically go back to the beginning for the next calculation.	[RST]
Tell calculator to stop learning. Reset the machine for the first calculation.	[LRN] [RST]

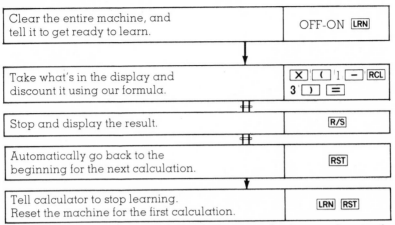

Enter your program carefully, following the keystrokes in the diagram.

Running It

The manager has decided to take 25% off shoes selling for $14.95, $17.99 and $18.99. Then he'd like you to mark 13% off books selling for $6.00, $7.99 and $12.50. What should the new prices be?

PRESS	DISPLAY/COMMENTS
[2nd] [Fix] 2	**0.00** This tells the machine to round the display value to the nearest cent
.25 [STO] 3	**0.25** Store the first discount rate as a decimal in memory 3

Enter old prices & press [R/S] to see new ones:

14.95 [R/S]	**11.21** ⎫
17.99 [R/S]	**13.49** ⎬ New prices
18.99 [R/S]	**14.24** ⎭

| .13 [STO] 3 | **0.13** Store the new discount rate |

Enter prices discounted for 13%, & press [R/S] to see new prices:

6 [R/S]	**5.22** ⎫
7.99 [R/S]	**6.95** ⎬ New prices
17.5 [R/S]	**15.23** ⎭

Note in this case that by storing the discount rate in memory 3, it's very easy to change rates as you move from department to department.

Next Stop

You'd like to keep track of all the marking up and down you do all day. Could you rewrite the above program to keep track of the *number* of items you've marked down in memory 4?

PAUSE FOR A REST STOP

Let's take time out from our examples for a moment to examine a very helpful feature of your calculator. You've already been briefly introduced to this feature in the first chapter — the "Pause" feature. Using it, you don't have to stop a program completely to get a quick look at what's happening at any point. All you need to do is insert the key sequence [2nd] [Pause] where you'd like to see a result. (Pause is the second function on the key labeled "SST".) Pause "stops the music" for about ¾ of a second. You can add more Pauses if you'd like a longer look.

Try the following short program to see this feature in action. We'll also be using the clear key ([CLR]) as part of the program — to clear things out as needed.

Turn your machine OFF and ON, then enter the following keystrokes:

[LRN]
1 [2nd] [Pause]
2 [2nd] [Pause]
3 [2nd] [Pause]
4 [2nd] [Pause]
5 [2nd] [Pause]
6 [2nd] [Pause]
7 [2nd] [Pause]
8 [2nd] [Pause]
[R/S] [CLR] [RST]
[LRN] [RST]

Can you guess what you'll see when you press [R/S] at this point? Try it. (To see it again, press [R/S] again.)

We'll be using the pause key at many points in programs where a quick glance is required. Try this one:

DESTINATION

Let's work up a program that adds the digits 1 through 9 and pauses for each result before the next digit is added. Here we'll be adding $1 + 2$, displaying 3, adding 3 to that, displaying 6, adding 4, displaying 10 and so on.

Making Tracks

First — try this one on your own! One possible program is shown for you below:

OFF-ON
[LRN]

1 [2nd] [Pause]
[+] 2 [=] [2nd] [Pause]
[+] 3 [=] [2nd] [Pause]
[+] 4 [=] [2nd] [Pause]
[+] 5 [=] [2nd] [Pause]
[+] 6 [=] [2nd] [Pause]
[+] 7 [=] [2nd] [Pause]
[+] 8 [=] [2nd] [Pause]
[+] 9 [=] [2nd] [Pause]
[R/S] [CLR] [RST]
[LRN] [RST]

Running It

Here just press [R/S] and you'll see 1, 3, 6, 10, 15, 21, 28, 36, 45. (Remember to allow for longer pauses just insert the [2nd] [Pause] key sequence 2 or more times. Also keep in mind, however, that each [2nd] [Pause] you insert uses up one of your 50 available program steps, so in your longer programs you may be limited as to how many pauses you use.)

Next Stop

Create a program that will multiply all the digits from one to 9 ($1 \times 2 \times 3 \times 4 \times 5 \times 6 \times 7 \times 8 \times 9$), and pause to show each result. *Note:* Your final result should be 362880.

GETTING AROUND:
A REVIEW OF LRN R/S RST STO RCL Pause

In this example we'll be putting together all of the techniques we've covered up to now. Imagine for a moment that you're currently employed by the Acme Can Top Company Incorporated, one of the world's leading manufacturers of can lids. As part of your job, you need to be able to quickly and accurately calculate the distance around any circular can lid (its circumference), and its area; given its diameter (the distance across its middle). The formulas for these calculations are shown in the diagram below:

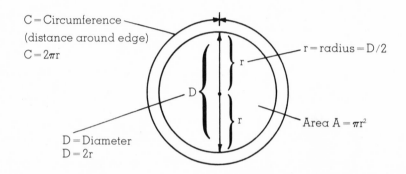

C = Circumference
(distance around edge)
C = 2πr

r = radius = D/2

D

r

r

Area A = πr²

D = Diameter
D = 2r

DESTINATION

Here we'd like to set up a program where we just enter the diameter D, press R/S and the circumference is displayed for about 2 seconds, followed by the area.

PLANNING THE ROUTE

Here the radius (r) (which equals ½ the diameter) is needed in both calculations. We'll calculate and store it in a memory right away. We'll then calculate the circumference by multiplying it by 2π, and pause a couple of times to look at it. To find the area, we'll recall the radius, square it, multiply by π, and stop.

MAKING TRACKS

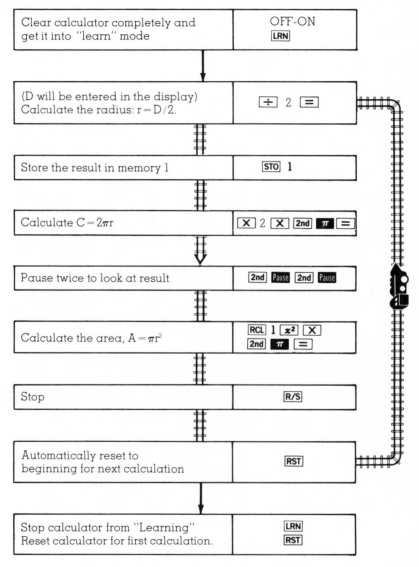

Clear calculator completely and get it into "learn" mode	OFF-ON [LRN]
(D will be entered in the display) Calculate the radius: r = D/2.	[÷] 2 [=]
Store the result in memory 1	[STO] 1
Calculate C = 2πr	[×] 2 [×] [2nd] [π] [=]
Pause twice to look at result	[2nd] [Pause] [2nd] [Pause]
Calculate the area, A = πr²	[RCL] 1 [x²] [×] [2nd] [π] [=]
Stop	[R/S]
Automatically reset to beginning for next calculation	[RST]
Stop calculator from "Learning" Reset calculator for first calculation.	[LRN] [RST]

Key in your program carefully from the above flow diagram.

RUNNING IT

Let's now say that you're confronted with 6 can lids and you've measured their diameters as follows:

10 cm	4 cm
13.61 cm	7.74 cm
30 cm	8.78 cm

You need to calculate the circumference and area of each, correct to 2 decimal places.

Just key in the following:

PRESS	DISPLAY/COMMENTS	
2nd Fix 2	**0.00**	Sets readout to 2 decimal places
10	**10.**	Diameter
R/S	**31.42**	Circumference
	78.54	Area
13.61	**13.61**	Diameter
R/S	**42.76**	Circumference
	145.48	Area
30	**30**	Diameter
R/S	**94.25**	Circumference
	706.86	Area
4	**4**	Diameter
R/S	**12.57**	Circumference
	12.57	Area
7.74	**7.74**	Diameter
R/S	**24.32**	Circumference
	47.05	Area
8.78	**8.78**	Diameter
R/S	**27.58**	Circumference
	60.55	Area

Note that the circumference will be in the same units as the diameter, and the area will be in those units squared.

NEXT STOP

Create a program to calculate the perimeter of a square (distance around it), and also its area:

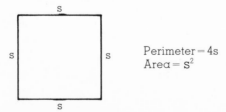

Perimeter = 4s
Area = s^2

FILL IT UP: LEAVING "HOLES" IN PROGRAMS

In some problem solving situations you'll need to enter several numbers into the calculation. In this example we'll show you how to leave "holes" in your program that you can easily insert numbers into as needed.

Let's continue our "Acme can lid problem" for a moment. This time you're in a situation where you'd like to be able to calculate the *volume* of any can that comes in. You can easily measure the *diameter* and the *height* of the can. The formula for calculating the volume is: $V = \pi r^2 h$

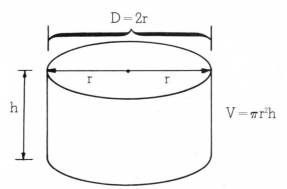

A key point here is that you have to enter *two* measurements into the formula. You must enter the diameter, D (from that you'll calculate $r = D/2$), and you must enter the height, h, to finish the calculation $V = \pi r^2 h$).

DESTINATION

You'd like to be able to calculate the volume of any cylindrical can, with as few keystrokes as possible.

PLANNING THE ROUTE

We'll show two ways to approach this problem:
a. You could store both D and h in memories and then recall them in a program to calculate the radius ($r = D/2$), then the volume ($V = \pi r^2 h$).
b. You could enter D, calculate $r = D/2$, square it, multiply by π, then press ⊠ and R/S. This halts the program and lets you enter h right from the keyboard. You then continue to complete the program with an ⊟ and R/S. What you do in this case is sort of "leave a hole" in the program to insert a number you'll need to work with.

Any "mixture" of these two methods is OK, too, depending on your personal approach to the problem.

MAKING TRACKS

Method a. In this method we'll assume that before we run the program we'll store the diameter (D) in memory 1, and the height (h) in memory 2.

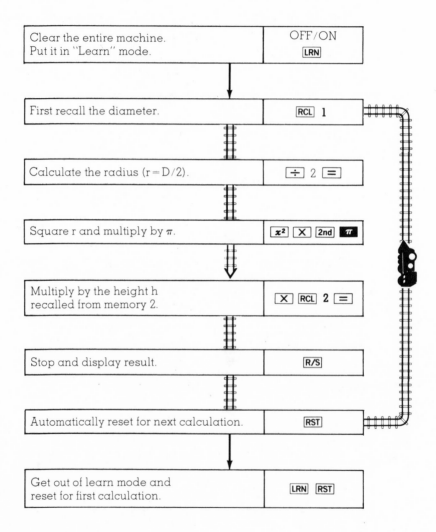

Clear the entire machine. Put it in "Learn" mode.	OFF/ON LRN
First recall the diameter.	RCL 1
Calculate the radius $(r = D/2)$.	÷ 2 =
Square r and multiply by π.	x^2 ✕ 2nd π
Multiply by the height h recalled from memory 2.	✕ RCL 2 =
Stop and display result.	R/S
Automatically reset for next calculation.	RST
Get out of learn mode and reset for first calculation.	LRN RST

To run this program, just key it in carefully from the flow diagram, then:
- Enter the diameter and press STO 1
- Enter the height and press STO 2
- Press R/S to display the volume, $V = \pi r^2 h$.

For example, calculate the volumes of these two cans accurate to two decimal places:

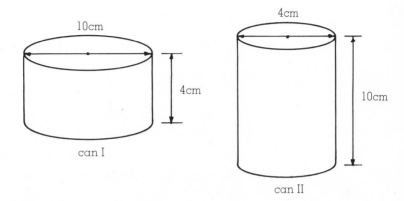

can I

can II

PRESS	DISPLAY/COMMENTS	
2nd Fix 2	**0.00**	Set display to readout 2 decimal places
10 STO 1	**10.00**	Enter diameter and store
4 STO 2	**4.00**	Enter height and store
R/S	**314.16**	Volume of can I
4 STO 1	**4.00**	Enter diameter and store
10 STO 2	**10.00**	Enter height and store.
R/S	**125.66**	Volume of can II

Method b. In this case, we'll write a program that allows us to just enter the diameter and press R/S. When the calculator stops, we'll enter the height and press R/S again. The final result will be the volume ($V = \pi r^2 h$).

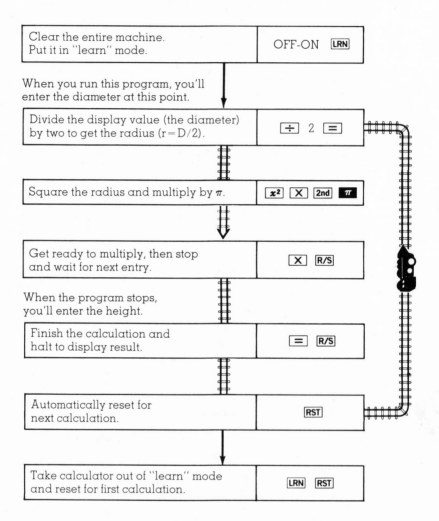

| Clear the entire machine. Put it in "learn" mode. | OFF-ON LRN |

When you run this program, you'll enter the diameter at this point.

| Divide the display value (the diameter) by two to get the radius ($r = D/2$). | ÷ 2 = |

| Square the radius and multiply by π. | x² X 2nd π |

| Get ready to multiply, then stop and wait for next entry. | X R/S |

When the program stops, you'll enter the height.

| Finish the calculation and halt to display result. | = R/S |

| Automatically reset for next calculation. | RST |

| Take calculator out of "learn" mode and reset for first calculation. | LRN RST |

To run this program:
- Enter the diameter and press R/S.
- Enter the height and press R/S.

The volume ($V = \pi r^2 h$) is displayed.

For our previous example, key in the new program carefully and then:

PRESS	DISPLAY/COMMENTS
[2nd] [Fix] **2**	**0.00** Set display to read out 2 decimal places
10	**10** Enter diameter and press [R/S]
[R/S]	**78.54** When calculator halts, enter height and press [R/S]
4 [R/S]	**314.16** The volume of can I
4	**4** Enter diameter of can II and press [R/S]
[R/S]	**12.57** When calculator halts, enter height and press [R/S]
10	**10**
[R/S]	**125.66** The volume of can II

NEW KEYS

In this example we used some old keys for some new tricks. We saw that you can get several numbers into a program in one of two ways:

- Store them in a memory before you run the program and then recall them when you need them, or
- Stop the program (make a "hole") and insert the numbers where you need them.

Any combination of these two methods is OK, too; just be careful to write down which memory is storing what or in which order things must be entered. (More about writing things down — "documentation" — will be covered later.)

NEXT STOP

Create a program that calculates the volume of any rectangular box:

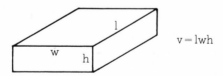

$$v = lwh$$

Create a program that calculates the longest side of a right triangle (the hypotenuse), given the other two sides:

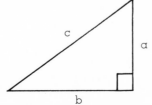

You'll use the "Pythagorean Theorem":

$$a^2 + b^2 = c^2$$

$$c = \sqrt{a^2 + b^2}$$

PROGRAM SIGN POSTS: [2nd] [Lbl] n and [GTO] n

Up to this point we have seen a variety of programs that handle "straight line" problems, "one way trips" so to speak. In the examples you've seen up to now, we've always started at the beginning, gone straight down to the nearest [R/S], and kept going from there when [R/S] was pushed again. In most of these programs, we used a [RST] (reset) to get back to the beginning, where we wanted to start things off.

There may be cases, however, where you would like to write one single program that covers several little problems you have to handle. Different sections of your program may have specific applications that you may want to use separately from other sections of the program. In cases such as this its handy to be able to start your calculator running somewhere *other* than the beginning of the program. You'd like to be able to pick and choose just where the train starts on its program track.

Your programmable calculator lets you do this pretty easily. You can start the program pointer, "the train on your track" at any preselected point you'd like to.

PROGRAM SIGN POSTS — LABELS

How do you "preselect" or identify various points in your program? This is where *LABELS* come in handy.

You can *label* any section of a program, or your entire program, by pressing the [2nd] [Lbl] key sequence, followed by one of the numbers 0 through 9. (Note that [Lbl] is the second function right over the [R/S] key, on the lower left of your keyboard.) There are a total of 10 labels (0-9) available for you to use in your calculator. These program labels are like little signposts you can use to mark certain points in your program. These make it easy for your calculator to find these points later on. Labels and labeling are an especially handy feature — and once you've labeled any point in your program it's very easy to get back to it using a variety of methods.

GTO —THE "Go To" KEY

One of the most straightforward keys on your machine is the GTO or "go
to" key. Once you've labeled a section of your program, (0-9), you can
tell your program pointer "train" to get to that point by simply pressing:

GTO **n** (where "**n**" is the number of the Label, 0-9).

Once the train is there, you just press R/S and it starts up, beginning right
where you told it to.

You can also use the GTO key while you're *writing* a program (in "learn"
mode). With the GTO instruction you can control the "flow" of your program
any way you'd like. If you want the sequence of the program to change,
or you'd like to skip to different sections of your set of keystroke
instructions, it's easy. Just label the points in your program that you need
to get to with the 2nd Lbl **n** key sequence. When you want the program
pointer to go to any of these points, just press GTO **n**.

You'll see more about how handy the GTO instruction is inside programs in
the next section. For now we'll show you an example of how the GTO key
can be used to let you pick any labeled point in a program as the
"starting point" for your program pointer.

EXAMPLE: AREA/VOLUME

Here's an example of how labels might come in handy. Let's say you find yourself in a situation where four separate mathematical tasks need to be done repetitively. One set of tasks might be:

1) Calculate the area of a square. $A = s^2$

2) Calculate the area of a circle. $A = \pi r^2$

3) Calculate the volume of a cube. $V = s^3$

4) Calculate the volume of a sphere. $V = \frac{4}{3}\pi r^3$

DESTINATION

You want to be able to enter the value of s (a side) or r (a radius), and then be able to apply the correct one of the 4 formulas shown to calculate an area or volume.

PLANNING THE ROUTE

Just key in each of these formulas as if it were a separate little program, but with the following added:

Put a label at the beginning of each formula with the **2nd** **Lbl** **n** key sequence (use label 1 for the first formula, 2 for the second, and so on).

Put an **R/S** at the end of each section, so that the program stops after the individual calculation is finished.

MAKING TRACKS

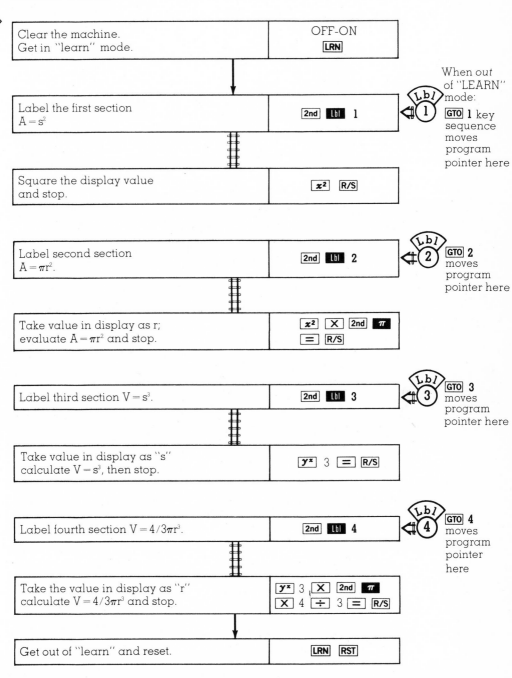

Clear the machine. Get in "learn" mode.	OFF-ON **LRN**

When out of "LEARN" mode:

Label the first section $A = s^2$	**2nd** **Lbl** 1

Lbl 1 — **GTO** 1 key sequence moves program pointer here

Square the display value and stop.	**x^2** **R/S**

Label second section $A = \pi r^2$.	**2nd** **Lbl** 2

Lbl 2 — **GTO** 2 moves program pointer here

Take value in display as r; evaluate $A = \pi r^2$ and stop.	**x^2** **X** **2nd** **π** **=** **R/S**

Label third section $V = s^3$.	**2nd** **Lbl** 3

Lbl 3 — **GTO** 3 moves program pointer here

Take value in display as "s" calculate $V = s^3$, then stop.	**y^x** 3 **=** **R/S**

Label fourth section $V = 4/3\pi r^3$.	**2nd** **Lbl** 4

Lbl 4 — **GTO** 4 moves program pointer here

Take the value in display as "r" calculate $V = 4/3\pi r^3$ and stop.	**y^x** 3 **X** **2nd** **π** **X** 4 **÷** 3 **=** **R/S**

Get out of "learn" and reset.	**LRN** **RST**

RUNNING IT

Key your program in carefully from the flow chart. At this point to use any one of the 4 parts of your program just key in the number you want to operate on and then:

- Press GTO
- Key in 1,2,3, or 4 — this selects the formula you want to use.
- Press R/S

EXAMPLE:
- Calculate the area of a square and the volume of a cube whose sides are 6.17 meters.
- Calculate the area of a circle and volume of a sphere whose radii are 2.98 cm.

PRESS	DISPLAY/COMMENTS	
2nd Fix 2	**0.00**	Set display to readout 2 decimal places
6.17	**6.17**	Enter first side
GTO 1	**6.17**	Select first label— $A = s^2$ program
R/S	**38.07**	Area of square (m^2)
6.17	**6.17**	Re-enter side
GTO 3 R/S	**234.89**	Volume of cube (m^3)
2.98	**2.98**	Enter radius
GTO 2 R/S	**27.90**	Area of circle (cm^2)
2.98	**2.98**	Re-enter radius
GTO 4 R/S	**110.85**	Volume of sphere (cm^3)

NEW KEYS

In this section we learned about two new and important keys:

2nd Lbl **n** (**n** from **0-9**) — Lets you label (or put a sign post) at any point in a program you need to get back to. You've seen in this section how labels work with the GTO key. In later sections you'll see other keys that use labels as part of their function.

GTO **n** (**n** from **0-9**) — Lets you start your program at any labeled point you'd like, or sends the program pointer to any labeled point you'd like.

NEXT STOP

Write a two-part program that will let you convert from Celsius (°C) to Fahrenheit (°F), or from Fahrenheit (°F) to Celsius (°C).

Use Label 1 for °C→°F: $°F = 9/5 °C + 32$
use Label 2 for °F→°C: $°C = 5/9(°F - 32)$

ROUND TRIPS:
AN INTRODUCTION

As you've seen in the section on *One Way Trips*, one of the primary benefits of programmability is that it takes a lot of the drudgery out of repetitive calculations. You can set up a keystroke sequence as a program *one* time, and from then on, easily operate with that keystroke sequence on any number you enter. In this section we'll move on to show you how your calculator can be set to perform repetitive calculations on its own — reading out results along the way. When your calculator is performing operations on its own, over and over again, it's said to be "in a loop" or "looping".

A "loop" is just a round trip for your program pointer "train". You can set things up so that your calculator will keep looping for weeks or even months with your recharger — until you manually stop things with the R/S key. Or, you can program your machine to perform a key sequence for a *specified number of times*. This section shows you how to set up "loops".

You've already seen some round trip loop programs in action in the very first chapter *Getting on Track*. As with all of the basic programming operations you're learning on your calculator, it's really very simple to do. Looping programs are especially useful, and are fun to watch in action, too — because your calculator is working on its own. It's interesting to think that it costs you little or nothing to have your calculator run loops for you — even if you have it looping for hours or days. On larger computers, where expenses often run hundreds of dollars an hour, running long loops can cost a fortune!

HELLO! LOOPS WITH THE RESET KEY: [RST]

The first program in this book — back in *Getting on Track* — used the simple technique you're about to see in action here to create a loop. All you do is put a [RST] keystroke at the end of your program while in learn mode — and *don't* insert any [R/S] instructions. Your program pointer moves down through your set of instructions, hits the [RST], turns around, "loops" back to the first instruction and starts down again. In this first example we'll examine a simple loop situation.

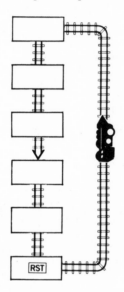

By placing [RST] at the end of a series of operations, with no [R/S] as part of the program, you create a continuous "looping" program. (This situation is sometimes called an *unconditional* loop.)

DESTINATION

Let's consider an example of an unconditional loop.

By now just about everyone's realized that when you flip your calculator over — upside down — certain of the numbers look like letters of the alphabet. (Some numbers do a better job of this than others.) With a little imagination you can see that the following numbers look like letters when the calculator is "flipped" over:

0 = O	3 = E	6 = g*	9 = G*
1 = I	4 = h	7 = L	
2 = Z*	5 = S	8 = B*	

*(These letters are tougher to "see" until you get used to them.)

As one loop example you can have your calculator display a message "neon sign" fashion over and over again. In this case — just to get a look at the process — let's create a program that displays "hello", over and over again.

MAKING TRACKS

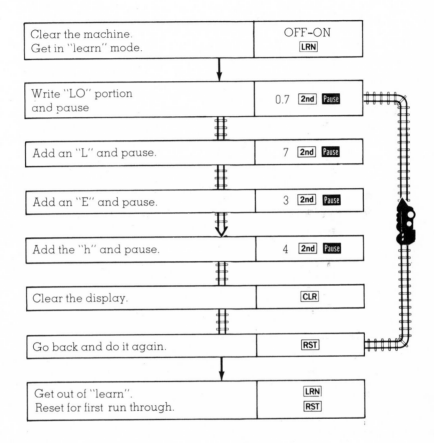

Clear the machine. Get in "learn" mode.	OFF-ON LRN
Write "LO" portion and pause	0.7 2nd Pause
Add an "L" and pause.	7 2nd Pause
Add an "E" and pause.	3 2nd Pause
Add the "h" and pause.	4 2nd Pause
Clear the display.	CLR
Go back and do it again.	RST
Get out of "learn". Reset for first run through.	LRN RST

RUNNING IT

Now your calculator is all set up to "print" the message. Just press R/S ,
flip the machine over, and there it is. (Programmers have been known to
spend hours thinking up clever things that their calculator can say — with
neon sign emphasis — to their friends and others.)

NEXT STOP

Write a program that displays the numbers 1 through 8 progressively in
the display:

1
12
123
etc. — pausing each time, clearing at the end, and repeating.

GRAPH WATCH!
LOOPS WITH [RST]

Often in school (and later on the job) it will be handy to *graph* the behavior of some mathematical function or "model" of some real life phenomenon. Your calculator in a loop is a natural for this. While it's in a loop, it can pause long enough to let you write down results in a table — or plot them right on a graph. (If it should start "getting ahead" of you — it's easy to stop things with the [R/S] key — then start them once more by hitting [R/S] again.)

In this example let's say you want to graph the distance an object travels in free fall — as it drops from an airplane, for example. Let's assume that it's a small, dense object like a brick — so that we can neglect wind resistance (at least until the brick is falling very fast). You need to plot the total distance it's fallen in feet for one-second time intervals. The equation that describes this process is:

distance fallen = $16 \times t^2$, when t is the time in seconds
    in feet   after the object is dropped

DESTINATION

You'd like to write a program where you simply press [R/S] and your calculator
- Displays a time t in seconds
- Pauses (2 times)
- Displays the distance the object has fallen at that time
            Distance = $16 \times t^2$,
- Pauses (3 times)
- Displays the next time (t + 1) — one second later, and so on

PLANNING THE ROUTE

First we'll store the current time in memory 1. Each time we go through the program we'll add one second to the current time in memory 1, recall memory one and display it (for 2 "pauses"). We'll then square it, and multiply by 16 to calculate the distance and display *that* for three pauses. At the end of our program, the last step will be [RST] to get things back to the beginning.

MAKING TRACKS

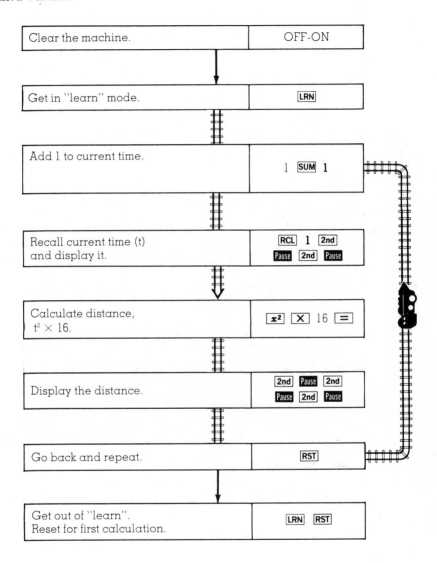

Clear the machine.	OFF-ON
Get in "learn" mode.	LRN
Add 1 to current time.	1 SUM 1
Recall current time (t) and display it.	RCL 1 2nd Pause 2nd Pause
Calculate distance, $t^2 \times 16$.	x^2 X 16 =
Display the distance.	2nd Pause 2nd Pause 2nd Pause
Go back and repeat.	RST
Get out of "learn". Reset for first calculation.	LRN RST

At this point you'd be all set to either write down time and distance in a table as shown on the next page, or graph them right on a graph. As we've mentioned — if the machine starts getting ahead of you, just stop things with the R/S key.

Another important point here is that your calculator can help you "feel" functions happening. Since it's displaying the function rapidly for you — you can get a good feel for how fast the distance "grows" in a free fall situation; or how fast your money grows if you double it once a day, as we've seen in the very first example in the book. This feature of learning with programming is a valuable one. Instead of just hearing or reading about how formulas and functions behave, you're *watching it happen*. You may find that some of the formulas you've been learning about take on a new life when you watch them in action on your calculator. At this point you know how to get almost any formula on the machine into a loop. Experiment! Watch functions "grow"

RUNNING IT

Enter your program carefully from the flow chart on the previous page. Then just get your pencil and table (or graph paper) all set and press [R/S] . You should see results like those below. (To stop things, just press [R/S] and hold it down momentarily until a number appears in the display.)

t(sec)	dist(feet)
1	16
2	64
3	144
4	256
5	400
6	576
7	784
8	1024
9	1296
10	1600
11	1936
12	2304
⋮	⋮

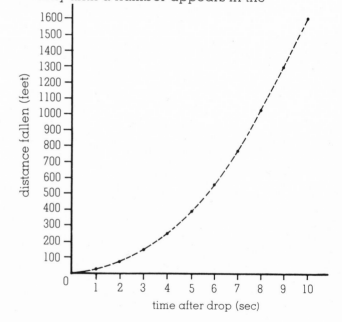

NEXT STOP

Write a program that will let you plot the function:

$$y = 2x^2 - 10x$$

for values of x:

$$x = 1, 2, 3, \ldots \text{etc.}$$

You'd like to have x displayed, then y, then x + 1, and so on.

COUNT OFF! LOOPS WITH GTO n AND 2nd Lbl n

You've already seen — and will continue to see — how it's often handy to be able to "count" inside your programs. There are many ways to accomplish this — and in the looping examples we'll discuss in this chapter we'll be showing you quite a few of them.

There are also quite a few ways to make loops or "round trips" happen for you. You've already seen how to do it easily with a RST at the end of your program. The RST key, however, always starts you right back at the beginning — so your whole program is "in the loop". There may be times where you'd like a "round trip" to involve just *part* of your program. Here's where the GTO key, working with labels, can be handy. To create a loop that only involves one part of your program just:

- Put a label where you want the loop to start with the 2nd Lbl n key sequence (**n** is one of your labels, 0-9).
- At the end of the "loop", make sure the last instruction is GTO n (where n is the same label number).

Here's a counting example that involves loops:

DESTINATION

You'd like to cook up a program that sets your calculator counting by 1's, 2's, 4's, etc. — whatever number you'd like. You'd also like to *start* counting *from* any number you select. The way you'd like things to work for you is as follows:

- You'll enter the number you'd like to count *by*, and press R/S
- You'll enter the "starting number" and press R/S . . .
  The calculator will then count by whatever number you've selected, beginning at your "starting number".

PLANNING THE ROUTE

In the first part of the program we'll store the first number entered — the number we're counting by — in memory 1. Then we'll store the *starting* number for our counting in memory 2. Now, after you've stored these two numbers, you won't want to return to this portion of the program for the counting sequence, so put down a label — telling the calculator this is the point to come back to in the "loop".

After the label, write the "counting" portion of the program. One way to do this is to recall the number you're counting by (in memory 1), and sum this to the starting number (in memory 2). This is the first number in the counting sequence, so recall memory 2 and pause to look at it. Then just repeat the process by returning to the label.

MAKING TRACKS

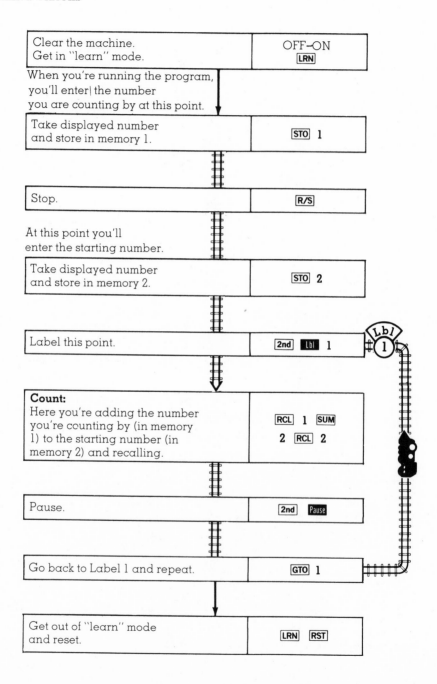

| Clear the machine.
Get in "learn" mode. | OFF–ON
[LRN] |

When you're running the program,
you'll enter| the number
you are counting by at this point.

| Take displayed number
and store in memory 1. | [STO] 1 |

| Stop. | [R/S] |

At this point you'll
enter the starting number.

| Take displayed number
and store in memory 2. | [STO] 2 |

| Label this point. | [2nd] [Lbl] 1 |

| **Count:**
Here you're adding the number
you're counting by (in memory
1) to the starting number (in
memory 2) and recalling. | [RCL] 1 [SUM]
2 [RCL] 2 |

| Pause. | [2nd] [Pause] |

| Go back to Label 1 and repeat. | [GTO] 1 |

| Get out of "learn" mode
and reset. | [LRN] [RST] |

RUNNING IT

Enter the program carefully from the flow chart. To start counting, simply:
- Enter the number you'd like to *count by* (say 5), and press R/S .
- Next, enter the number you'd like to start with (say 120), and press R/S again.

Your calculator will start counting:

$$125.$$
$$130.$$
$$135.$$
$$140.$$
$$145.$$
.
.
.

NEXT STOP

Write a program that lets you take any number you'd like, and raise it to powers that go up from zero in steps you select. For example, you enter a 13, press R/S , enter 2, press R/S and the results

1.	(or 13^0)
169.	(or 13^2)
28561.	(or 13^4)
4826809.	(or 13^6)
etc.	

are displayed. (Use the y^x key.)

CASH IN THE BANK-
LOOPS WITH [GTO] n AND [2nd] [lbl] n

Let's consider another more ''close to home'' type of application for your calculator. One major advantage of being able to program repetitive calculations is that it's easy to play the game of ''what if?'' What if you had $3000 in a savings account for 6 years? How fast would it grow? Are there other better places to put it? What if you need $1500 of it after 2 years?

Before devices like your calculator came along, weighing alternatives in situations like this could be quite tedious — even with a ''regular'' calculator helping out! Now you can have the calculator pushing its own buttons for you as a decision-making helper. Consider the following situation:

DESTINATION

You'd like to have a program that ''grows'' a sum of money just as if it were in a savings account. To use it, you'd like to:

- Enter the amount of cash you're tucking away in your account, and press [R/S]
- Enter the yearly interest rate and press [R/S] again.
- Then — you'd like the calculator to display — at yearly intervals — just how much your money grows — year by year (its future value). You'd like the year, then the future value displayed.

PLANNING THE ROUTE

The formula to use for watching your cash grow is:

future value = present value $\times (1+i)^n$

where i is the yearly interest rate expressed as a decimal, and n is the number of years you've left your money in the bank.

Here we'll be taking the first number entered in the display (the present value of the cash we're putting in the account) and storing it in memory 1.

We'll take the second entered number (yearly interest as a decimal), and we'll store it in memory 2.

At this point we'll set up a label (we'll use label 1) — because we'll be using a loop to calculate our cash growth. After the label, we'll step up the year by one, display it, and then evaluate the cash growth formula.

The last step of our program will be a [GTO] 1 — to complete the loop.

MAKING TRACKS

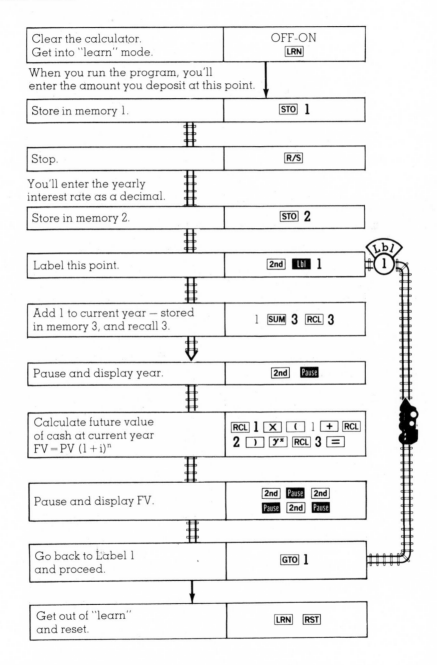

Clear the calculator. Get into "learn" mode.	OFF-ON LRN

When you run the program, you'll
enter the amount you deposit at this point.

Store in memory 1.	STO 1

Stop.	R/S

You'll enter the yearly
interest rate as a decimal.

Store in memory 2.	STO 2

Label this point.	2nd Lbl 1

Add 1 to current year — stored in memory 3, and recall 3.	1 SUM 3 RCL 3

Pause and display year.	2nd Pause

Calculate future value of cash at current year $FV = PV (1 + i)^n$	RCL 1 X (1 + RCL 2) y^x RCL 3 =

Pause and display FV.	2nd Pause 2nd Pause 2nd Pause

Go back to Label 1 and proceed.	GTO 1

Get out of "learn" and reset.	LRN RST

RUNNING IT

Enter your program carefully from the flow chart above. Press [2nd] [Fix] 2 so that your results will be displayed in "dollars and cents" format. Then

- Enter your cash deposit, say $1000, press [R/S], and the display will show **1000.00**
- Enter the yearly interest rate (for 6% enter .06) and press [R/S] again.

Your display should then read out:

1.00	First year
1060.00	Value of cash at end of first year
2.00	Second year
1123.60	Value of cash at end of second year
3.00	Third year
1191.02	Value of cash at end of third year
4.00	Fourth year
1262.48	Value of cash at end of fourth year
etc.	

When you'd like to stop, just press and hold down the [R/S] key for a moment. You can "try out" or "what if" with any cash value or interest rate you'd like. Just press [INV] [2nd] [C.t] [RST] to clear all the memories and begin at the first step, then proceed as before.

NEXT STOP

Develop a program that will let you start with any number:

- Display its square.
- Increase the number by 0.5 and display it.
- Display the new square.
  etc.

CONTROLLED ROUND TRIPS:
LOOPS WITH [2nd] [Dsz] [GTO] n

In this section we're introducing a new and powerful key sequence for "making loops happen" in your calculator. This particular feature lets you *select exactly how many times* you'd like to go around a loop. After a selected number of times around you can send the program pointer "train" on to other tasks or stop it — whichever you like. This feature we're speaking of uses the [2nd] [Dsz] [GTO] n key sequence. ([Dsz] is the second function of the [GTO] key — on the left middle of your keyboard.) [Dsz] stands for the words (watch these carefully):

> **d**ecrement
> and
> **s**kip
> on
> **z**ero.

The "decrement and skip on zero" key sequence works with *memory zero* to allow you to set up loops. Here's how it works:

You just enter the number of times you want the calculator to go "around the loop" — any positive integer in this case — and store it in memory zero. From then on in, whenever the program pointer comes to a [2nd] [Dsz] [GTO] n key sequence, several things will happen:

> First, the calculator subtracts one from whatever positive integer is stored in memory 0 ("decrements" it by one).
> Then it examines the result:
> > — If the result is *not* zero, the program pointer goes right on to the [GTO] n instruction step that immediately follows the [2nd] [Dsz]
> > — If the result is zero, the program pointer *skips* (hops right over) the [GTO] n step immediately following the [Dsz] , and moves on to whatever step is listed *next*.

Got all that? Once you get the hang of it, setting up loops using the [2nd] [Dsz] [GTO] n key sequence is really pretty easy. You can set up a loop to any labeled point in your program, for as many times as you like. The [2nd] [Dsz] is really just a "lap counter". You tell your calculator how many times you want to go around the loop by storing that number in memory 0. The program pointer "train" goes around the loop that number of times, and then skips on to whatever instruction comes next. Here's a picture of what happens:

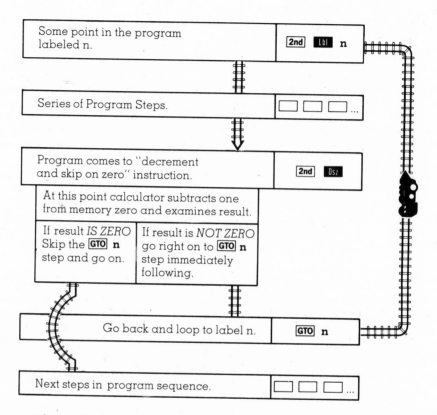

Let's consider a simple example:

DESTINATION

Cook up a program using the [2nd] [Dsz] [GTO] n instruction sequence that counts up to whatever number you enter into the display. You'd like to enter a number into the display, press [R/S] and have the calculator count up to that number and stop, pausing at each count.

PLANNING THE ROUTE

Here we'll enter the number of loops needed into the display and store it right away in memory zero, then clear the display. We'll plant a label right after the clear instruction for setting up the loop. Then we'll add one and pause. At this point you need to create the "controlled loop" back to your label with the [2nd] [Dsz] [GTO] n key sequence. After the display has counted up to the number stored in memory zero, you want it to halt — so end things with an [R/S] .

MAKING TRACKS

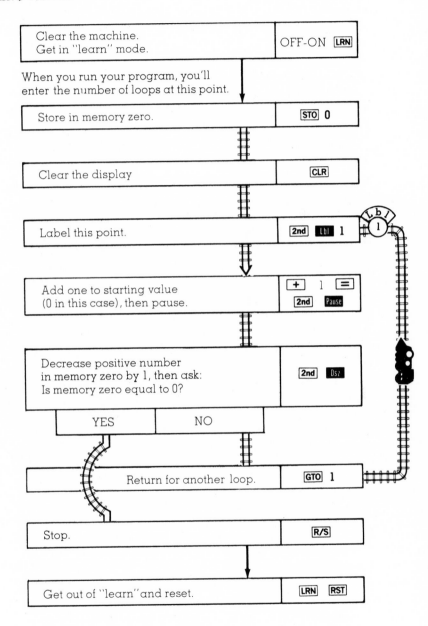

| Clear the machine. Get in "learn" mode. | OFF-ON [LRN] |

When you run your program, you'll enter the number of loops at this point.

| Store in memory zero. | [STO] 0 |

| Clear the display | [CLR] |

| Label this point. | [2nd] [Lbl] 1 |

| Add one to starting value (0 in this case), then pause. | [+] 1 [=] [2nd] [Pause] |

| Decrease positive number in memory zero by 1, then ask: Is memory zero equal to 0? | [2nd] [Dsz] |

| YES | NO |

| Return for another loop. | [GTO] 1 |

| Stop. | [R/S] |

| Get out of "learn" and reset. | [LRN] [RST] |

RUNNING IT

Carefully key in your program from the flow chart. Then just enter any number you'd like to count up to - (say 10), press R/S and your display should read:

> 1.
> 2.
> 3.
> 4.
> 5.
> 6.
> 7.
> 8.
> 9.
> 10.

Then, things should stop. To count to any other number, just enter it and press RST R/S .

NEW KEYS

In this section we've introduced a powerful key sequence for setting up "controlled loops". The 2nd Dsz GTO n key sequence lets you "loop" to any labeled point in your program, for the number of loops you enter into memory zero.

As you'll continue to see as you go through this book, the 2nd Dsz key sequence is quite a powerful and versatile program instruction. There are many places where you'll find this operation useful — and we'll try to introduce you to these applications areas one at a time. (No doubt you'll find some of your own unique applications as you move on in programming.)

NEXT STOP

Develop a program that causes your calculator's display to count *down* from any number you enter in the display to one, pausing at each count.

FACTORIAL!
LOOPS WITH 2nd Dsz GTO n

An idea that crops up often in studies of probability and statistics is what's called the *factorial* of a number. The *factorial* of a number is indicated with an exclamation point "!". So, "17 factorial" is written 17!. If you've ever wondered how many ways 17 people could arrange themselves in 17 chairs — the answer is 17!. The factorial of any number, say 5, is calculated by multiplying the number "out" as follows:

$$5! = 5 \times 4 \times 3 \times 2 \times 1$$

The factorial of any number, N, is equal to:

$$N! = N \times (N-1) \times (N-2) \ldots \ldots \times 1.$$

(The number 0! is defined to be 1.)

DESTINATION

Write a program that allows you to enter a number (say 17), press R/S, and have its factorial calculated and displayed.

PLANNING THE ROUTE

This example is a "natural" for use of the 2nd Dsz GTO n key sequence to generate the numbers 17, 16, 15, . . . 3, 2, 1 in memory 0. We'll enter our number, load it in memory zero, and put in a label (Label 1) right after that point. Then, we'll recall memory zero, hit the multiply key and then enter the 2nd Dsz GTO 1 key sequence. You can visualize the loop something like this:

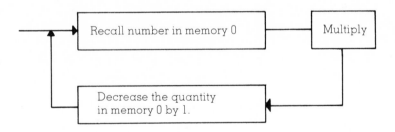

If the first number placed in memory 0 is 17, then the first time around the loop would produce 17 X, and the quantity in memory 0 would be reduced to 16. After the next loop you would have 17 X 16 X, and 15 would be stored in memory 0. This loop would continue to generate the required series for the factorial.

After this loop has "finished" and memory 0 is at 0, we'd like to see the results of all the products. However, since the last thing the calculator is told to do is X, an = cannot immediately follow as X = produces an error signal. To avoid this, you can put a "1 =" at the end of the program, and the "final product" X 1 = gives the correct result.

MAKING TRACKS: FACTORIAL PROGRAM

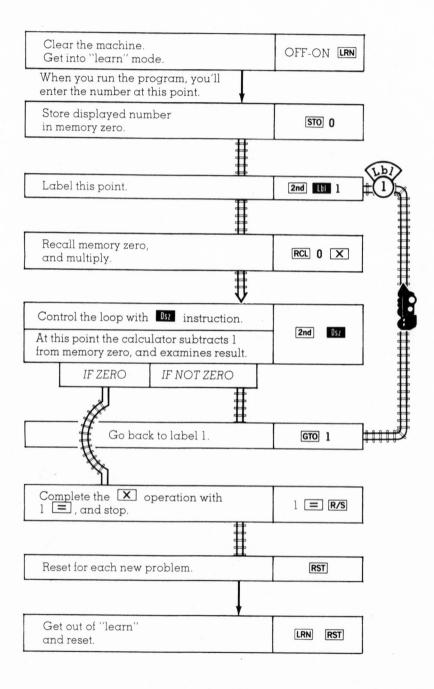

Clear the machine. Get into "learn" mode.	OFF-ON `LRN`
When you run the program, you'll enter the number at this point.	
Store displayed number in memory zero.	`STO` 0
Label this point.	`2nd` `Lbl` 1
Recall memory zero, and multiply.	`RCL` 0 `X`
Control the loop with `Dsz` instruction. At this point the calculator subtracts 1 from memory zero, and examines result.	`2nd` `Dsz`
IF ZERO *IF NOT ZERO*	
Go back to label 1.	`GTO` 1
Complete the `X` operation with 1 `=` , and stop.	1 `=` `R/S`
Reset for each new problem.	`RST`
Get out of "learn" and reset.	`LRN` `RST`

Running It

Enter the program carefully from the flow chart. Once entered, to calculate the factorial of any number (positive integer less than 70), just enter it and press [R/S].
Some examples:

Press	Display/Comments
5 [R/S]	**120.** or 5!
10 [R/S]	**3628800** or 10!
17 [R/S]	**3.5568743 14** or 17!
50 [R/S]	**3.0414093 64** or 50!

Notice that this last calculation keeps your calculator busy for quite some time. Remember any time you put your machine into a loop — give it time to crank out the result. Some loops can take hours — even days! Note also that this program will give you an incorrect result for 0! If you enter 0 and press [R/S] — the result is zero, not 1 as it should be. You might want to develop a program where you do not get an incorrect result for 0!. (Techniques you'll be learning later on will help.)

As we've already mentioned, using the [2nd] [Dsz] key sequence will come in handy in a variety of situations. In this section we've introduced a few of its most straight-forward uses. In later sections we'll be speaking more on the "ins and outs" of its application.

Next Stop

Develop a program that displays the factorial of the numbers 1, 2, 3, 4, . . . etc. You'd like each integer displayed for two pauses, then its factorial displayed for three.

AN INTRODUCTION

Up to this point we've been running through some shorter programs to show you how easy it is to get into action with your calculator. By now it's probable that somewhere along the line you've made a mistake (a missed keystroke, a RST key left out, etc.). When this happens (and it happens to even the most experienced calculator users), often the simplest thing to do is turn your machine OFF and ON, and re-key your program carefully. There will be cases, however, where you'd like to be able to correct or just change programs you have in the machine. There will also be times where, even when you haven't made any keystroke errors, there's a mistake in your programming logic that causes trouble.

Well, your calculator has several special features designed just to help you in these situations. With these features you can:

- Check over program keystrokes to see just what is "where" in your program.
- Insert or delete keystrokes to correct errors, or change what a program does for you.
- Easily get to any part of a program that needs "fixing".

In this chapter we'll be introducing these *editing* features, and we'll be talking a bit about recommended ways to "write up" or *document* your programs — to make them easy to get back to and use even long after you've first written them. We'll also mention some of the basics on program troubleshooting.

FINDING PROGRAM STEPS: KEY CODES AND [SST] [BST]

How Your Calculator Remembers Steps

At this point, let's talk a bit on how your calculator goes about remembering program steps you teach it. It's not really magic; your calculator just has a separate, special memory — called the *program memory* — that remembers *keystrokes* for you. You "turn on" this memory when you first press the [LRN] key. Your calculator then remembers the keystrokes you enter, until you press [LRN] again (or enter too many steps). You know when you're in "learn" mode — and your program memory is working — because your display takes on the unique format: **00 00.**

Now, the way that your calculator remembers the keystrokes is also pretty simple. It remembers each keystroke you enter in "learn" mode as a number — called a *key code*. Each programmable key sequence on your machine has a numerical code that your calculator stores in its program memory. When you run a program, the program pointer runs through the program steps, and as it comes to each code it "pushes" the key or keys each code represents.

The [SST] and [BST] Keys

To take a look at some of this in action, we'll go back to the very first program we covered in *Chapter 1* and check out its key codes. There are two special keys that help you do this checking out:

[SST] The *single step* (forward) key lets you step through a program one step at a time
—either while in "learn" mode to check out key codes, as we'll see
or
— when not in "learn" mode, to move your program pointer "train" one step at a time — and actually run a program keystroke by keystroke — checking out what's in the display at each point.

[BST] The *backstep* key moves you one step at a time, but in reverse. Again, if you're in "learn" mode you'll go backwards through your program and be able to check out key codes in reverse. (The [BST] key doesn't function when you're out of "learn" mode.)

Let's see all this in action! First, let's key in our simple program that takes whatever is in the display, doubles it, pauses and then repeats:

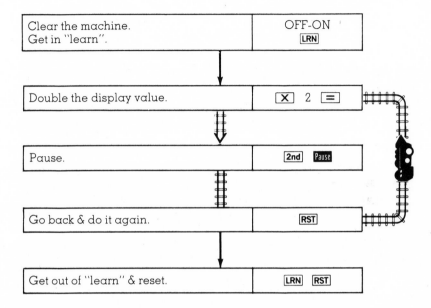

Clear the machine. Get in "learn".	OFF-ON LRN
Double the display value.	X 2 =
Pause.	2nd Pause
Go back & do it again.	RST
Get out of "learn" & reset.	LRN RST

Now, instead of running this program, let's check out its key codes — the codes that store what we told the calculator to do.
Press LRN .
Notice now that the display reads

00 55

This special display format is designed to let you easily examine and keep track of key codes:

- The *left* two digits of the display are the program step counter, or *what step number you're at in your program.* (The first step is numbered 00 and numbers continue up to the last allowable step 49, for a total of 50 steps.)
- The *right* two digits display the code for the keystroke instruction at that step.

Because we pushed reset, the program step counter digits are 00, the first of our possible 50 steps. The right pair of numbers (55) is the key code for multiply, thatcorresponds to your first program step. We'll examine all of the key codes in a minute, but first let's step through our program and watch what happens at each program step.

PRESS	DISPLAY/COMMENTS
[SST]	**01 02** at step 01 (2nd step).
	02 is the code for digit ''2''
[SST]	**02 85** At step 02 (3rd step), 85 is the code for [=]. At this point we've told the calculator to take the display, multiply it by 2 and display the results
[SST]	**03 36**
	36 is the code for pause
[SST]	**04 71**
	71 is the code for RST or reset
[SST]	**05 00**
	A zero, or in this case, nothing, is at step 05
[SST]	**06 00**
	Again nothing

At this point, we've reached (and gone past) the end of our program. Now move backwards with the [BST] key:

[BST]	**05 00**
[BST]	**04 71**
	At this point, we're back to the [RST] instruction
[BST]	**03 36**
	Back to the pause instruction (and so on).

We can [SST] or [BST] anywhere in our program. However, *one important point about [SST] and [BST]* : they *cannot become part of any program in your calculator.* When your calculator is in the ''learn'' mode, all that pressing [SST] or [BST] does is move you through the program steps and show you the step number and key code. When you're out of ''learn'' the [SST] key moves your program pointer through the steps one a time — and you can watch the results in the display. (As we said before, the [BST] key does nothing when you're not in ''learn'' mode.)

To watch the [SST] key in action in stepping through your program while out of "learn", just press the [LRN] and [RST] keys, then press [CLR] and enter a one in the display. Then begin pressing [SST] :

PRESS	DISPLAY/COMMENTS
[SST]	1. Step 1 [×]
[SST]	2 Step 2
[SST]	2. Step 3 [=]
[SST]	2. Step 4 [2nd] Pause
[SST]	2. Step 5 [RST]
[SST]	2. Step 1 [×]
[SST]	2 Step 2 2
[SST]	4. Step 3 [=]
[SST]	4. Step 4 [2nd] Pause
[SST]	4. Step 5 [RST]

Often at this point in learning about key codes folks will ask, "Why can't I see these key codes *while* I'm programming my machine? All I see on the right side of the display are zeros when I'm keying a program in." The reason for this is that while you're in "learn" mode keying in keystrokes, the display *jumps ahead* to the next step location in your program memory as soon as you enter any program step. As soon as you enter a step the display moves on to the next blank instruction space — waiting for your next instruction. So, to actually see the key codes, you need to:
   • Press [LRN] to get out of "learn" mode.
   • Press [RST] to get back to the beginning of your program.
   • Press [LRN] again.
   • You can now go through your program and check the key codes with the [SST] and [BST] keys — and see things one step at a time.

KEY CODES

Now, how do you (and your calculator) know what the number codes are for all the keys and key sequences on your calculator? Actually, it's simple — *the key code for any key is just the row and column position of that key.* Look at the keyboard diagram below:

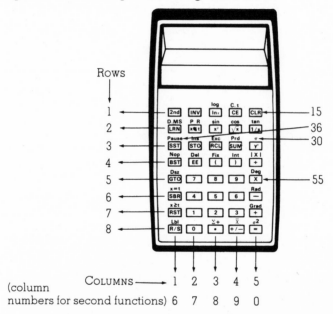

There are *8 rows* of keys (numbered 1 to 8 top to bottom), and 5 columns of keys (numbered 1 to 5 left to right.). The key code for any first function key is a two-digit number: the first digit is the *row* the key is in, the second digit is the *column* it's in.

Look at the $\boxed{\text{CLR}}$ key. It's in the first row and fifth column, so its key code is 15. The multiplication key ($\boxed{\times}$) is in the fifth row, fifth column, so its code is 55, and so on.

For second functions (written right over the keys) the column numbers are 6, 7, 8, 9, 0 as shown. For example, the $\boxed{\text{2nd}}$ $\boxed{\text{Pause}}$ key sequence has 36 as its code (for row 3, column 6). Notice that the right-most column for second functions has the digit number zero (instead of 10). So, the key code for second functions in the 10th column will just show a row number and 0. For example, notice the $\boxed{\text{2nd}}$ $\boxed{\pi}$ key sequence. Its key code is 30: row 3, column 0. A complete table of these codes is in *Appendix F* of this book. The key code logic is easy to remember — so even without the table you can pretty well keep track of key codes as you go on in your programming.

SPECIAL NOTES ON KEY CODES

There are several situations where you'll see some special behavior
when looking over the key codes. Let's go through three of these special
cases.

First . . . For the numbers 0 through 9, the key code is simply the number: 0
is 00, 1 is 01, 2 is 02, etc. Numbers you enter into a program just stay as
numbers and not a separate code.

Second . . . A three-number code (called a merged code) is used when
you use certain keys on your machine. This is true for all of the keys that
require either a memory or label number immediately after them. Turn
your calculator OFF and ON and try this example:

PRESS	DISPLAY/COMMENTS
[LRN]	**00 00**
[STO]	**00 32 0** The 00 32 0 shows the code for step 00 will be "store" (32) but the memory location (0-7) must be entered next (in the place of the last 0).
1	**01 00** Memory 1
[GTO]	**01 51 0** The 01 51 0 shows the code for step 01 will be "go to" (51) the label number (0-9) entered next (in the place of the last 0).
2	**02 00** Label 2
[LRN]	**0**

We didn't really write or finish this "program", but it will show you the
three number code we were talking about.

PRESS	DISPLAY/COMMENTS
[RST]	**0**
[LRN]	**00 32 1** This means that the first step, step 00, is to *store* (the 32 code) in memory 1 (the extra or 3rd number on the right)
[SST] (to step to next step)	**01 51 2** This means that the second step, step 01, is go to (the 51 code) label 2 (the extra or 3rd number on the right)

Third . . . The [INV] or inverse key when used with certain keys as part of a program will give the standard key code with a *negative sign* in front of it. Since the [INV] means to "undo" or reverse a function, the key code is the same as for the function, but the negative sign will tell you it's the *inverse* of the key and not the key itself.

To check this out on your calculator, first turn it OFF and ON to clear everything and then:

PRESS	DISPLAY/COMMENTS
[LRN]	**00 00**
[2nd] sin	**01 00**
[INV] [2nd] sin	**02 00**
[LRN]	**0.**

Again, this isn't a program that will do anything, but let's just examine its key codes:

PRESS	DISPLAY/COMMENTS
[RST]	**0** Reset machine to first program step
[LRN]	**00 28** Step 00 is sine (code 28)
[SST]	**01 -28** Step 01 is the *inverse of sine* (or "arcsine")

Again, any time you see a negative key code, it indicates the *inverse* of that keyboard function.

KEYS WITHOUT CODES

For some important reasons, there are several keys that are not given separate key codes:

[2nd] and [INV]

The [2nd] and [INV] keys that we've talked about don't have codes because they are *always* used with another key that does have a code.
The [INV] key just puts a negative sign in front of a standard key code, as we've discussed.

[LRN]

Since this key is only used to go in and out of the "learn" mode, it doesn't have a code. [LRN] itself can never be part of a program.

[SST] and [BST]

As we mentioned earlier, these just step us forward or backward through the program without affecting the program. Since they can't become part of a program, they don't need a code. Two new and important keys which we'll discuss in the next section — (keys that let us correct errors and change programs) — also don't have key codes. These are the "insert" and "delete" key sequences:

[2nd] [Ins] and [2nd] [Del]

These key sequences actually are designed to let you modify a program while in "learn" mode, and cannot become *part of* a program.

MAKING CHANGES AND CORRECTIONS

At this point you've seen how you can check out the key codes of any program you have entered in your calculator. To review the process one more time:

- First, be sure you're *out* of "learn" mode
- Press RST
- Press LRN

Then step through your program, forward or backward, with the SST and BST keys and check the key codes for each step.

Now, if you find a wrong key code, or should you want to alter the functions of your program, there are three basic methods available to change or *edit* the steps in your program.

REPLACING ONE STEP WITH ANOTHER

You can *at any step*, simply replace the step that's already there with a new one. While you're in "learn" mode, right at the step you'd like to replace, just *enter the new step right over the old one*. The new keystroke sequence will just replace the old one. Note that as soon as you enter a new program step the *calculator's display* will skip right to the *next step*. The step number and key code you'll see *right after* you've replaced a given step in your machine is the *next* one in your program. If you want to go back and see the new key code for the step you just entered — press the BST key. In this way you can check changes you've just made.

EXAMPLE: Let's consider one quick case using our "Double the Display Value" program again. First, key it in:

OFF-ON
LRN
× 2 =
2nd Pause
RST
LRN

Now, let's say we'd like to change this program so that it multiplies the number in the display by 5, instead of 2. Here's what you do:

PRESS	DISPLAY/COMMENTS
RST	**0** Get back to beginning of program
LRN	**00 55** You're at the first step — " × "
SST	**01 02** This is the 2 that multiplies the display value. Just enter 5 at this point.
5	**02 85** Display jumps to next step " = "
BST	**01 05** Go back to check on your correction. 5 has replaced 2.

INSERTING OR
DELETING STEPS 2nd Ins 2nd Del

In addition to just replacing program steps with new ones, your calculator will automatically handle the operations involved in inserting additional steps, or deleting unwanted steps. Two new key sequences — the *insert* — 2nd Ins — and *delete* — 2nd Del — sequences, do this for you. Here's how to use these new keys:

To INSERT STEPS:

• While in "learn" mode, using the SST or BST keys, get to the program step where you'd like to add additional keystrokes. For example, if you want to insert some keystroke sequence between steps 07 and 08 in a program, SST to step 08. (You go to step 08 because step 07 is O.K., but you want new information inserted at step 8.)

• Press 2nd Ins . This takes the instruction at this program step, and all the ones that follow it, and "pushes them down" one step. This leaves a blank instruction at the point where you'd like to insert a new one.

• Key in the new instruction.

• You can continue this sequence of adding program steps: 2nd Ins , then key in the new instruction, as many times as you need to — provided that your overall program doesn't exceed the limit of 50 steps.

If you exceed the limit, 2nd Ins will push the last instruction "off", and you'll lose it.

Note: Whenever you key in your new instruction (or instructions), the display will jump to the next step. If you'd like to check the key codes on instructions you've just inserted — use the BST key.

To DELETE STEPS:

• While in "learn" mode, using the SST or BST keys as needed, get right to the step you'd like to delete.

• Press 2nd Del . The unwanted step will be deleted, and all the steps that follow it will be "brought up" one step to fill the space it leaves. The display at this point will show the same step number, with a new key code — the code of the step that followed the one you deleted.

EXAMPLE:

Let's put all of these editing features together in an example. Let's say that for some assignment you need to solve the equation $y = 2x^2 + 4x$ for several values of x. First, write a program to do this:

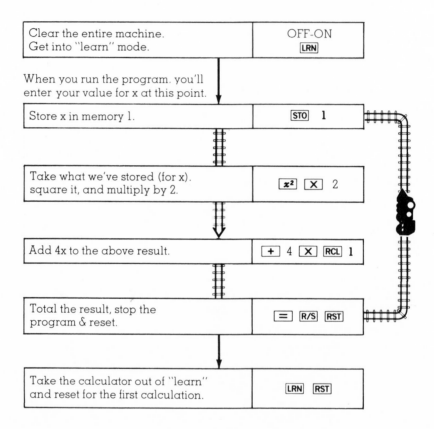

| Clear the entire machine.
Get into "learn" mode. | OFF-ON
[LRN] |

When you run the program. you'll enter your value for x at this point.

Store x in memory 1.	[STO] 1
Take what we've stored (for x). square it, and multiply by 2.	[x²] [X] 2
Add 4x to the above result.	[+] 4 [X] [RCL] 1
Total the result, stop the program & reset.	[=] [R/S] [RST]
Take the calculator out of "learn" and reset for the first calculation.	[LRN] [RST]

Now, let's check the program. Find y when x = 2.

PRESS   **DISPLAY/COMMENTS**
2 [R/S]   **16.**
               When x = 2, y = 16

We can also check our program by checking the key codes.

PRESS		DISPLAY/COMMENTS
[CLR] [RST]		0
[LRN]		00 32 1
[SST]		01 23
[SST]	Then [SST] through the program to see	02 55
.	that your key codes match your	03 02
.	program. (As you might expect, it's a	04 75
	good idea to write down your	05 04
	program. This helps you check it and	06 55
	also save it for future reference. We'll	07 33 1
	show you a suggested form for this	08 85
	later.)	09 81
		10 71

Now let's say you have a need to change this program. Maybe another problem has come up, and now you need to evaluate the equation $y = 2x^2 - 4x + 7$.

At first glance you may want to just key in a new program, but in many cases you may find it easier to change the program you already have. All you need to do is change the $+4x$ to a $-4x$ (the plus to a minus), and tack the "$+7$" on at the end. We'll make these changes one at a time, starting on the next page.

First, remember that you can change any program step to a new one simply by going to that step and, while in the "learn" mode, keying in the new step right over the old one. If you look at the program steps on the previous page, you'll see that the [+] is at step 04 (key code 04 75). To change this, first press [LRN] to get *out* of "learn" mode, then press [RST] . Then follow these steps:

PRESS	DISPLAY/COMMENTS
[LRN]	00 32 1 First program step
[SST]	01 23
[SST]	02 55
[SST]	03 02
[SST]	04 75 Step you'd like to change

At this point, just key in the new step

| [−] | 05 04   Display jumps to the next step |
| [BST] | 04 65   New code at step 4 — we've changed the "plus" to a "minus". |

Now, let's move on and tack a +7 on the end of our original program. The key code for the [=] key is 85, and if you look back to the original key code listing, you'll see that this is step 08 in the original program. We'd like to insert a " +7" at that point — so step to 08 with the [SST] key.

[SST]	05 04
[SST]	06 55
[SST]	07 33 1
[SST]	08 85

Now use the "insert key sequence".

[2nd] [Ins]	08 00 The display shows that step 8 is now clear — ready to have a new step inserted.
[+]	09 85 Display jumps to next step. Note the 85 key code. The [=] has been moved down to step 09.
[2nd] [Ins]	09 00 Step 9 now clear
7	10 85 Again the display jumps to next step. [=] has been moved to step 10.
[BST]	09 07 "[7]" at step 9.
[BST]	08 75 "[+]" at step 8.
	All our changes have been made correctly!
[LRN]	0
[RST]	0

You're now ready to run the edited program.
To solve for y, when x = 2, 3, and 5:

2 [R/S]	**7.**
3 [R/S]	**13.**
5 [R/S]	**37.**

Now, to see the *delete* key sequence in action, let's go back and undo what we've done in our edit, and change the program back to evaluating $y = 2x^2 + 4x$.

To do this, we need to change the minus back to plus, and delete the "+7". Here's what to do:

PRESS	DISPLAY/COMMENTS
[CLR] [RST]	**0**
[LRN]	**00 32 1**
[SST]	**01 23**
[SST]	**02 55**
[SST]	**03 02**
[SST]	**04 65** This is the code for [−] · we need to change to [+] .
[+]	**05 04**
[BST]	**04 75** go back & check, then go on
[SST]	**05 04**
[SST]	**06 55**
[SST]	**07 33 1**
[SST]	**08 75** [+] key at step 08 — we need to delete next two steps
[2nd] [Del]	**08 07**
[2nd] [Del]	**08 85** Now 85 code [=] is where it belongs, and "+7" has been deleted.

At this point, you've completed your changes on the program, so press [LRN] and [RST]. To check the program, enter 2 and press [R/S]. If the result is 16, your edit was successful. If not, you now have the power to review the key codes and check for problems.

GOING RIGHT TO
THE PROBLEM [GTO] [2nd] n n

At this point you've seen how to use the [SST] and [BST] keys to get to any point in your program — and how to change things by writing over program steps you'd like to change, or using the [Ins] or [Del] keys to add or take away steps. There's another key sequence that helps you "get right to" any point in a program, to help you locate problems or just check on the codes. This is a special sequence involving the [GTO] key. You've already seen how the [GTO] n instruction can be used in a program to create loops, or to move the program pointer "train" to any labelled location in the program that you'd like.

The [GTO] key can also be used when you're *out* of "learn mode" — to get you to any step of a program. You can go directly to any step you need to with the [GTO] [2nd] nn key sequence — where **nn** is the (two-digit) *step* number you'd like to go to. Here's how it works:

THE GTO 2nd nn KEY SEQUENCE:

- Be sure you're *not* in "learn" mode
- Press GTO 2nd nn, where nn is the step number you'd like to get to (01, 05, 21, etc.)
- When you press LRN, you'll be at that step number.

As an example, let's key in our quick program that doubles the display value one more time, and go to various parts of it with the GTO 2nd nn key sequence:

PRESS	DISPLAY/COMMENTS
OFF-ON	0
LRN	00 00
× 2 =	03 00
2nd Pause	04 00
RST	05 00
LRN RST	0

Then we can get to any step easily:

GTO 2nd 02	0.
LRN	02 85 We're at instruction number 2 (=) in our program.
LRN	0 Get *out* of "learn" mode
GTO 2nd 04 LRN	04 71 — the RST instruction
LRN	0.
GTO 2nd 28 LRN	28 00 We're at instruction space 28 — no program instructions here
LRN	0
GTO 2nd 61	0. (Flashing) We've tried to go beyond step 49 — the last allowable step — an error condition.

Using the GTO 2nd nn key sequence can be a genuine time saver — particularly in checking, editing or troubleshooting longer programs! Keep in mind, however, that this sequence *cannot be used as part of a program.* (You must use the GTO n sequence where n is a label if you need a "go to" instruction in a program.)

"WRITING UP" PROGRAMS: DOCUMENTATION

As you continue to learn about programming, you'll find that there are some especially handy programs that you'd like to save for future use. To enable you (and other friends or colleagues) to use your programs at some later time, it's a good idea to take a moment to write them up so that you can use them later. A pad of "Program Record" forms — designed to make it easier for you to write up programs — is included with your calculator.

The Program Record form is divided into the following sections to facilitate program writeup while you create the program:

- At the top of the form are spaces for the program title, your name and the date; in the lower right hand corner is a space for a three-digit program number you can assign to each program for easy and accurate program record keeping.

- The *Program Description* section lets you write "in words" exactly what the program does and what equations/information, etc. it uses to do it.

- The *How to Use It Section* lets you write down the keystroke sequence for using the program (once it's correctly entered into the calculator). There's room to let you insert *sample data* — so you can check out the program for correct operation after it's keyed in.

The information above can (and should) be written down *before* you begin writing a program. In this way, you have a clear destination in mind as you set down program keystrokes.

- On the back of the Program Record form there's an area labelled *Flow Chart/Notes* — to enable you to write up a condensed flow chart or extra notes on your program. You may be able to actually develop your programs in this area.

- To the immediate right of this area — there are columns for recording *keystrokes, step numbers and key codes* — as well as *comments* about "where you are" at important points in your program.

Notice that the "Key" and "code" columns are each divided into three sections. This is to let you write on one line any key sequence that requires one program step. Key sequences involving the **2nd** and **INV** keys (or both), as well as those that require a label or program number following them — can be entered on a single line.

Once you've keyed in your program, and you're sure it's working correctly, you can press [RST] [LRN], and then use the [SST] key to step through and write down each program key code. In the three columns in the "code" section — you can write on one line those instructions whose codes include a minus sign, label or memory number.

- The lower left of this side of the form provides special charts allowing you to easily record what's stored in the *memories*, or what program segments are identified with *labels*. These are especially easy to forget — and so it's quite important to record them.

A sample form — filled out for you — is shown here. The idea in writing up programs is to record things so that any friend of yours (with the same calculator) could pick up the form — and use and understand your program right away.

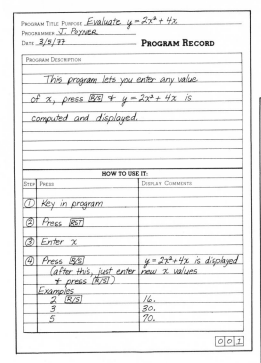

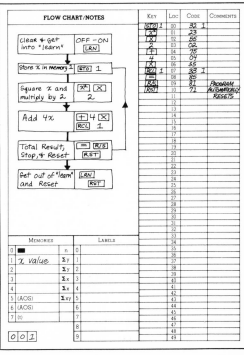

BASIC TROUBLESHOOTING

Even the most careful person makes mistakes from time to time. Your calculator is easy and straightforward to use, but sometimes through a programming oversight — even when you've carefully keyed things in — your program won't work properly. Here are a few tips and things to look for in troubleshooting basic programs.

Your calculator will let you know about errors in a program in one of several ways. If at any point in a program an inaccurate key sequence or series of operations creates an error condition (see *Appendix C*), *the program will stop* and show you a flashing display. This simply means that you've asked the calculator to do something in a program that it couldn't normally do even from the keyboard.

Exceeding the display limits or using an incorrect key sequence will "stop the music". In other cases you may *not* see a flashing error condition, but the results of your program are just plain wrong. It's always good practice to verify the accuracy of a program with test input data, whose program outcome you *know*. If you don't get the result expected, it's time to look for a problem.

When a program is not working — try to "think like the machine". Go through your flow chart (and key codes) and execute — *blindly* — whatever it says to do there. You may find that you've inadvertently boxed your program into some corner. The [SST] key can be of help — both in and out of "learn" mode, in tracking just what may have gone wrong.

[RST] — Be sure you've reset the calculator wherever you need to — to get back to the beginning of the program. Also, be sure to turn the machine OFF and ON before beginning a new program — to clear everything.

— Algebraic Operating System

Remember that all the power of the **AOS**™ algebraic entry system is working for you — even inside programs. All operations will be carried out following the correct mathematical hierarchy. This order *may not* correspond to the order of entry you've used in your programs.

Remember that your calculator will hold up to *4 pending operations*, at any one time.

If you have any doubts about the order in which expressions are being evaluated — remember that you can insert parentheses — [( ] [ )] — to be certain that things are evaluated in the order you specify.

Remember that special (single variable) function keys must *follow* the number they work on. If you want the sine of 30° at some point in a program, the keystroke sequence is 30 [2nd] [sin]

[=] **Key** — this completes any and all pending operations waiting to happen inside your machine — be careful using it. (Be careful of using [=] in subroutines — discussed later. It's better to use [( ] [ )] keys to complete calculations when in a subroutine, because [=] will complete calculations in the main program as well.)

Labels — Be sure you use any one of the 10 labels *no more than* once in any program.

Angular mode — If you're using any of the trig functions, remember that when you first turn the calculator on it interprets all angles as degrees, unless you change things with the [2nd] [Rad] or [2nd] [Grad] key sequences, and stays there until you change again (or turn the calculator OFF-ON).

Memories — Be careful to check and see that all operations using memories are working with the *correct memory*. Also, note that if you have 4 operations pending in any expression in your program — that memories 5 and 6 will be used to hold some of the expressions. Any numbers stored previously in memories 5 and 6 will be lost if a long expression involving 4 pending operations is entered later on. (Also, memory 7 is the "t" register — you'll be learning more about it in the next section.) Memory zero is the memory used with the [2nd] [Dsz] key sequence — keep that in mind, too.

You'll find that with a little experience your programs will run accurately and with little trouble. You'll also develop an "eagle eye" for a potential problem area once it's hit you one time — so the best way to learn troubleshooting is to keep using your calculator. After awhile you probably will rarely need to troubleshoot any of your programs.

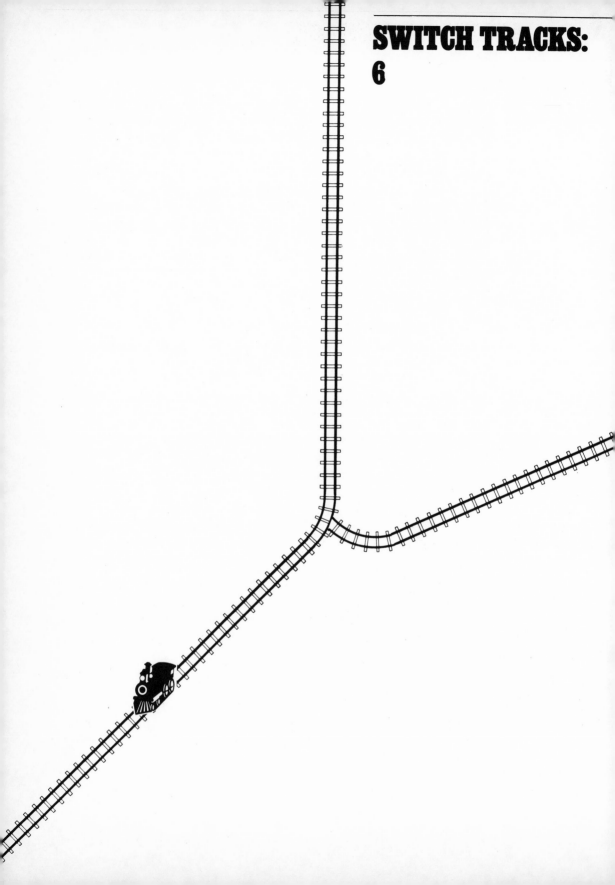

AN INTRODUCTION

There are several keys on your calculator which give it the power to make decisions while in a program. These keys are straightforward to use, and basically, they allow you to make comparisons between what is in the display (or, more properly, the *display register*), and some *test* number or value. Based on how the display register and test register values compare (equal, unequal, greater than or equal to, less than), the calculator will take different program paths. In this chapter we'll cover each of the decision-making keys and features of your calculator. The keys and key sequences we'll be discussing include:

[x↔t]	Exchange x and t
[2nd] [x=t]	Is x equal to t?
[INV] [2nd] [x=t]	Is x not equal to t?
[2nd] [x≥t]	Is x greater than or equal to t?
[INV] [2nd] [x≥t]	Is x less than t?

We'll introduce each of these features and key sequences first; then we'll go through examples of how to use each of them as part of a program.

THE "TEST" OR "t" REGISTER AND THE [x↔t] KEY

One of the memories in your calculator, memory *seven*, is set aside to handle tests. For this reason, memory 7 is called the "test" or "t" register. As you'll be seeing, many decisions in your calculator can be set up as a comparison of the "display register" and the "t" register. Since memory 7 is so special, there are several ways to get numbers into it:

- One way is to just enter the number and press [STO] **7**.
- Another way is to enter the number and press the [x↔t] key. This key just "swaps" what's in the display register for what's in the "t" register (memory 7). (By the way, the words "register" and "memory" actually mean the same thing.)

Keep in mind that [x↔t] is *not* a "store" operation but an "exchange" operation. (Actually, it is just a handier, single key equivalent to the [2nd] [Exc] **7** key sequence which performs the identical function.)

When you press [x↔t] the value in the display register gets stored in the "t" register (memory 7), and what was in the "t" register gets put into the display register.

DISPLAY AND "DISPLAY REGISTER"

As we've mentioned, the decision-making power of your calculator involves comparing two numbers, then taking different program paths based on how they compare. These two numbers will be the number in the "t" register, and the number in the *display register*. The display register is also called the "x" register; whenever you see an "x" on your keyboard ([1/x] , [√x] , etc.), the x is referring to the number in the display register. One point to keep in mind is that the *display register* holds numbers up to 11 digits, while your calculator's *display* only shows you 8 of them (correctly rounded).

This, in most cases, is not a very significant matter, but we are pointing it out now for a good reason. Those last three digits in the display register — the ones you can't see — can affect comparisons your calculator makes. The *displayed number* you see in the "x" register and "t" register may be equal, but the last three digits may still not agree. In a case such as this, the calculator will say that x is *not* equal to t if it makes a comparison.

As we have said, this is seldom a problem for most of your calculations and programs. When problems arise on this point, however, they can be really irksome if you don't know the reason why. One way to avoid this problem is to insert the key sequence [EE] [INV] [EE] . This sequence following a number will truncate the guard digits of a result leaving only the rounded display value for further use (see Appendix D).

THE COMPARISON INSTRUCTIONS:

There are four ways to compare what's in the "x", or display register, with what is in the "t", or test register (memory 7). Each of these four key sequences makes a comparison and asks a question. If the answer to the question is "yes", your program pointer will go right on to the keystroke sequence immediately following the comparison. If the answer is "no", the program pointer *skips* the keystroke sequence immediately following the comparison and keeps on going. We'll list how these comparisons work for you, then show you a program example of each one in action.

1. **2nd** **x=t** — "Is x Equal to t?"

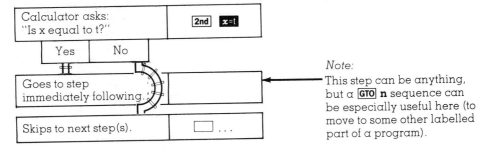

Note:
This step can be anything, but a **GTO** **n** sequence can be especially useful here (to move to some other labelled part of a program).

2. **INV** **2nd** **x=t** — "Is x Unequal to t?" $(x \neq t)$

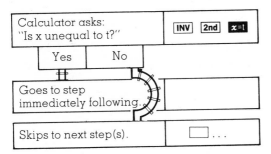

3. **2nd** **x≥t** — "Is x Greater Than Or Equal To t?"

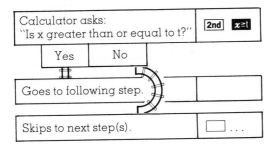

4. **INV** **2nd** **x≥t** — "Is x Less Than t?" $(x < t)$

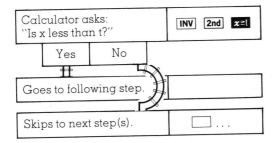

COUNTING UP
EXACTLY: $x{\rightleftarrows}t$ 2nd $x=t$

In this first example, we'll show you a straightforward way to use the
2nd $x=t$ key sequence.

DESTINATION

Write a program that uses the 2nd $x=t$ instruction and counts (by one)
from zero up to any number you enter. You'll just enter the number, press
R/S and the calculator will count up to the number and stop (pausing at
each count).

PLANNING THE ROUTE

We'll take the displayed number and put it in the "t" register right away
with the $x{\rightleftarrows}t$ key. Then we'll clear the display and plant a label. We'll
"count" by adding 1 to the display and pausing. We'll test to see if we've
reached our stopping point with a 2nd $x=t$ key sequence. When x = t
we'll want to stop the program. For all x values less than t we'll want to
keep counting.

MAKING TRACKS

Enter the program carefully from the flow chart on the next page.

RUNNING IT

PRESS	DISPLAY/COMMENTS
5	5
RST R/S	0
	1.
	2.
	3.
	4.
	5.

At this point you can enter any new number you would like to
count to, press RST and R/S, and watch your calculator count up
to it.

NEXT STOP

A. Edit the program in this example so that it automatically resets itself
   after each "counting session" — ready for new number entries.
B. Write a program that counts down from any number you enter to zero,
   then stops, using 2nd $x=t$

MAKING TRACKS

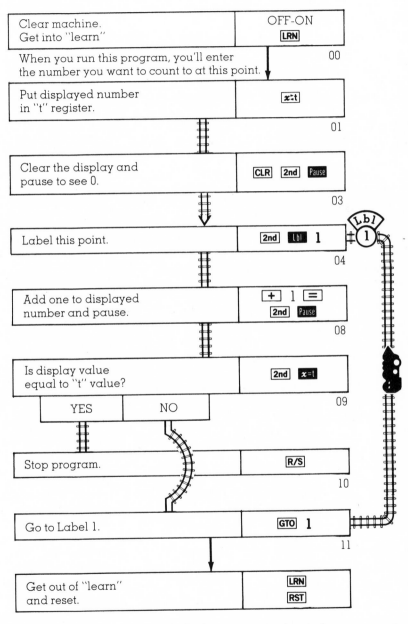

Clear machine. Get into "learn"	OFF-ON [LRN]

When you run this program, you'll enter
the number you want to count to at this point.   00

Put displayed number in "t" register.	[x⇄t]

01

Clear the display and pause to see 0.	[CLR] [2nd] [Pause]

03

Label this point.	[2nd] [Lbl] 1

04

Add one to displayed number and pause.	[+] 1 [=] [2nd] [Pause]

08

Is display value equal to "t" value?	[2nd] [x=t]
YES NO	

09

Stop program.	[R/S]

10

Go to Label 1.	[GTO] 1

11

Get out of "learn" and reset.	[LRN] [RST]

Note: From now on, to help you keep track of your program keystrokes as you enter them,
we'll include the step number you'll see *as you enter the program*, right below each
program keystroke box. This is the step number you'll see in the display when you're first
entering the program in "learn" mode, after you've completed entering the keystrokes in
that box.

THE SAME BIRTHDAY:

| $x{\gtrless}t$ | INV | 2nd | $x{=}t$ |

In this example we'll be taking a look at an interesting problem from the field of probability that will illustrate the use of the INV 2nd $x{=}t$ key sequence.

If you are in a room with several people, what are the chances that two of you have the same birthday? (The answer may surprise you!) The solution to this problem is a "classic" — and it's a natural for your programmable calculator to handle.

The usual way to handle this problem is in *reverse*. First consider how you would calculate the probability that *no* two people in the room would have the same birthday. Then subtract that result from 1 to get the probability of the reverse outcome.

Start by considering one person. Whatever the day, he or she has a birthday. The probability that another person does *not* have the same birthday is $\frac{364}{365}$. The probability that a third person does not have the same birthday is $\frac{363}{365}$, and so on. So, if five people are in a room together, the probability that *none* of these folks has the same birthday is:

$$\frac{364}{365} \times \frac{363}{365} \times \frac{362}{365} \times \frac{361}{365} = 0.9728644.$$

The probability that two of these folks *do* have the same birthday is one minus this: 0.0271356, or about 2.7%. Note that in solving this problem you keep multiplying numbers divided by 365: $\left(\frac{364}{365} \times \frac{363}{365} \times \frac{362}{365} \times ... \right)$. You'll have *one less* of these numbers than the number of people you're considering.

DESTINATION

Using INV 2nd $x{=}t$, write a program that calculates the chances (as a percent) that two people in any room have the same birthday. You'd like to enter the number of folks in the room, press R/S , and have the probability of two people with the same birthday displayed.

PLANNING THE ROUTE

We'll place the number of loops needed (the number of people minus 1) in the t register and then use INV 2nd $x{=}t$ for a branch to get the correct number of loops. We'll store 365 in memory 2 and then generate the numbers 364, 363, 362, ... for each loop by subtracting one from memory 2 and then storing in memory 2 again. For details follow the logic as you enter the program from the flow chart on the next page.

MAKING TRACKS

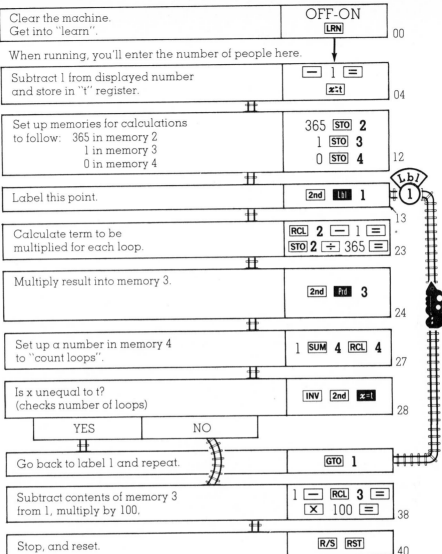

Clear the machine. Get into "learn".	OFF-ON [LRN]	00

When running, you'll enter the number of people here.

Subtract 1 from displayed number and store in "t" register.	[−] 1 [=] [x⇄t]	04

Set up memories for calculations to follow: 365 in memory 2 / 1 in memory 3 / 0 in memory 4	365 [STO] 2 / 1 [STO] 3 / 0 [STO] 4	12

Label this point.	[2nd] [Lbl] 1	13

Calculate term to be multiplied for each loop.	[RCL] 2 [−] 1 [=] / [STO] 2 [÷] 365 [=]	23

Multiply result into memory 3.	[2nd] [Prd] 3	24

Set up a number in memory 4 to "count loops".	1 [SUM] 4 [RCL] 4	27

Is x unequal to t? (checks number of loops)	[INV] [2nd] [x=t]	28

YES	NO

Go back to label 1 and repeat.	[GTO] 1	

Subtract contents of memory 3 from 1, multiply by 100,	1 [−] [RCL] 3 [=] / [×] 100 [=]	38

Stop, and reset.	[R/S] [RST]	40

Get out of "learn", reset & fix decimal at 1 place.	[LRN] [RST] / [2nd] [FIX] 1	

RUNNING IT

Just enter the number of people in any group and press [R/S] to see the probability that two of them have the same birthday. For example:

PRESS	DISPLAY/COMMENTS
5 (people)	**5**
[R/S]	**2.7** (2.7% chance that 2 folks have the same birthday).
25 [R/S]	**56.9** (56.9% chance)

Notice how long you keep your calculator busy during these long "loop" calculations!

RENT-A-CAR?
DECISIONS WITH [2nd] [x≥t]

Any situation where a series of calculations must be repeated many times is an excellent place for your programmable calculator to save time and increase accuracy. The "behind the counter" calculations repeated daily in many businesses is one example. Let's say you're in the Rent-A-Car business, where the mileage charge is $0.15 per mile for the first 100 miles, and $0.12 per mile for all miles above 100.

DESTINATION

You would like to work up a program where you just enter the number of miles, press [R/S], and the calculator computes and displays the correct total charge.

PLANNING THE ROUTE

You have two situations here. If the mileage is under 100 miles, you just need to multiply the number of miles by 0.15. If the number of miles is above 100, you will charge $15.00 for the first 100 miles and $0.12 per mile for all miles over that. Your total is then: 15 + (number of miles driven − 100) × $0.12. Since the number of miles driven is used in both formulas it will be stored at the beginning of the program (in memory 1). Your calculator can select and evaluate the proper formula for you by asking: "Is the number of miles driven greater than or equal to 100?" The keystrokes [2nd] [x≥t] will ask this question for you if the number of miles driven is in the display and 100 is placed in the "t" memory (memory 7). If the number of miles driven is greater than or equal to 100 the program pointer will execute the step immediately following [2nd] [x≥t], otherwise, that step is skipped.

MAKING TRACKS

Follow the program logic and enter the steps carefully from the flow chart on the next page.

RUNNING IT

To use the program, just enter the mileage, and press [R/S]. As an example, calculate charges for 250, 101 and 37 miles:

PRESS	DISPLAY/COMMENTS	
250 [R/S]	**33.00**	charges—250 miles
101 [R/S]	**15.12**	charges—101 miles
37 [R/S]	**5.55**	charges— 37 miles

NEXT STOP

Edit the above program to allow you to also add in a $12.00/day charge in addition to the mileage charge above. You'd like to be able to enter the number of days, press [R/S]; enter the mileage, press [R/S] again, and have the calculator display the total charges.

MAKING TRACKS

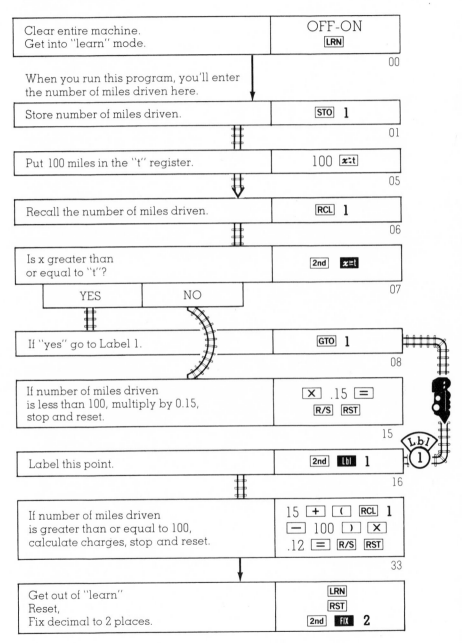

Clear entire machine. Get into "learn" mode.	OFF-ON [LRN]
	00

When you run this program, you'll enter
the number of miles driven here.

Store number of miles driven.	[STO] 1
	01

Put 100 miles in the "t" register.	100 [x≷t]
	05

Recall the number of miles driven.	[RCL] 1
	06

Is x greater than or equal to "t"?	[2nd] [x≷t]
	07

YES	NO

If "yes" go to Label 1.	[GTO] 1
	08

If number of miles driven is less than 100, multiply by 0.15, stop and reset.	[×] .15 [=] [R/S] [RST]
	15

Label this point.	[2nd] [Lbl] 1
	16

If number of miles driven is greater than or equal to 100, calculate charges, stop and reset.	15 [+] [(] [RCL] 1 [−] 100 [)] [×] .12 [=] [R/S] [RST]
	33

Get out of "learn" Reset, Fix decimal to 2 places.	[LRN] [RST] [2nd] [FIX] 2

MAKING TRACKS INTO PROGRAMMING

FOLLOW THE BOUNCING BALL!
LOOPS WITH [INV] [2nd] [x≥t]

There are a variety of situations where setting up limits on a loop may be handy. In this case the [2nd] [x≥t] or [INV] [2nd] [x≥t] key sequences can be very useful. Consider an example you may find from a basic physical situation. A new toy ball on the market, "dynamoball", claims to bounce to 85% of its height on each bounce. As part of a lab exercise you need to plot what the ball's behavior *should* be, then you'll experiment with a ball to see if it meets the manufacturer's claim.

DESTINATION

You'd like to write a program that lets you enter the initial height of the ball (in centimeters) off the ground, press [R/S] and have the "bounce number" and height of the bounce displayed for several pauses each — (long enough to write it down). When the height of the bounce becomes less than 1 cm, you'd like the calculator to stop.

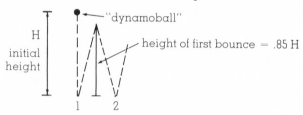

PLANNING THE ROUTE

We'll take the initial height and store it immediately. We'll put a 1 in the "t" register (since we want the calculator to stop when the height is less than 1), and then place zero in memory 2. We'll sum 1 to memory 2 to display the "bounce number". Then we'll recall the height (in memory 1) multiply by .85, and store the result back in memory 1, and pause (This displays the height of each bounce.) Then, we'll check to see if the bounce height is less than 1. If it is, we'll stop; if not, we'll go back and calculate another "Bounce".

MAKING TRACKS

Follow the program logic and enter the program carefully from the flow chart on the opposite page.

RUNNING IT

Try entering 5, as the initial height, and press [R/S]. The result:

Bounce #	Height	Bounce #	Height
1.000	4.250	6.000	1.886
2.000	3.613	7.000	1.603
3.000	3.071	8.000	1.362
4.000	2.610	9.000	1.158
5.000	2.219	10.000	0.984

6

MAKING TRACKS

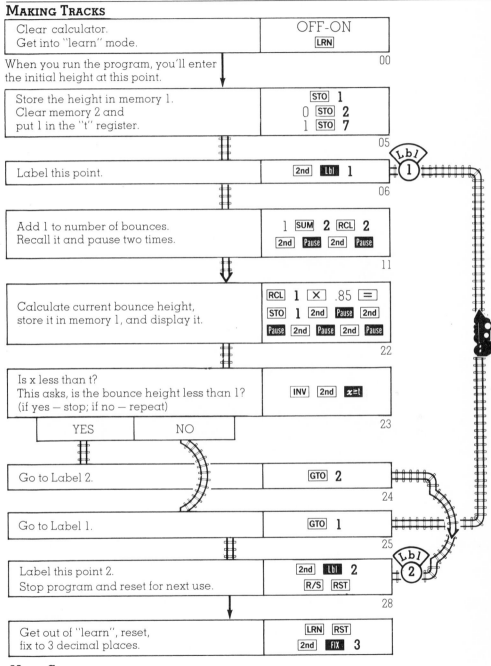

Clear calculator. Get into "learn" mode.	OFF-ON [LRN]

When you run the program, you'll enter the initial height at this point.   00

Store the height in memory 1. Clear memory 2 and put 1 in the "t" register.	[STO] 1 0 [STO] 2 1 [STO] 7

05

Label this point.	[2nd] [Lbl] 1

06

Add 1 to number of bounces. Recall it and pause two times.	1 [SUM] 2 [RCL] 2 [2nd] [Pause] [2nd] [Pause]

11

Calculate current bounce height, store it in memory 1, and display it.	[RCL] 1 [×] .85 [=] [STO] 1 [2nd] [Pause] [2nd] [Pause] [2nd] [Pause] [2nd] [Pause]

22

Is x less than t? This asks, is the bounce height less than 1? (if yes — stop; if no — repeat)	[INV] [2nd] [x≥t]

23

YES	NO

Go to Label 2.	[GTO] 2

24

Go to Label 1.	[GTO] 1

25

Label this point 2. Stop program and reset for next use.	[2nd] [Lbl] 2 [R/S] [RST]

28

Get out of "learn", reset, fix to 3 decimal places.	[LRN] [RST] [2nd] [FIX] 3

NEXT STOP

Develop a program that calculates the value of y in the equation
$y = 4x^2 - 3x$, for x = 1, 2, 3, 4, etc. The program should stop when the value of y exceeds 100.

SHORT HOPS: "SUBROUTINES"
[SBR] AND [INV] [SBR]

At this point you've come quite a long way in learning about programming. As we move on toward the completion of the programming section of this book, we'll be covering a few of the special features of your calculator that contribute to what we'll call its "advanced" programming power. One such feature is the "subroutine" feature of your machine. As its name implies, a subroutine is a "sub" or "mini" program that may come in handy — particularly if some task is repeated many times within your program. You can take any series of steps and make it into a subroutine easily on your calculator with the **Lbl** and [SBR] keys.

Here's how it works. If you need a sequence of keystrokes over and over again as part of a program, you can (while programming):
- Put a label ([2nd] **Lbl** **n**) in front of the series of keystrokes
- Enter the keystrokes as you would normally
- *Important:* At the end of the series of keystrokes finish with the key sequence [INV] [SBR]

When you need to execute the entire series of keystrokes, all you need to do is insert the key sequence [SBR] **n.**

This single key sequence then operates with *all of the* instructions you've put in the subroutine, and the program then moves on normally. Here's a diagram of what happens:

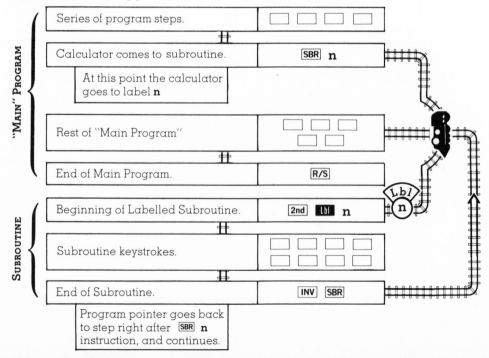

SOME ADVANTAGES OF SUBROUTINES:

There are several important advantages in using subroutines as part of your programs.

You can use a subroutine as many times as you need to in your program. (By the way, "using" or "accessing" a subroutine is often referred to as "calling it".)

You can use the SBR **n** key sequence *right from the keyboard* (while *not* in "learn") too. When you press this sequence from the keyboard the program pointer goes right to label n, and starts up. The calculator keeps on working until it hits INV SBR, or R/S, then it stops. This way you can use subroutines right off the keyboard, without using the "main" program itself.

Your calculator is equipped with *2 levels* of subroutine capability. This simply means that while you're inside one subroutine you can "call" another one. (One subroutine can call another one.) You *cannot*, however, have a subroutine call a subroutine that in turn tries to call up a third one.

Using subroutines can mean a huge savings in program steps and a genuine boost to your programming efficiency. Anytime you use a set of keystrokes in a program more than once, use of a subroutine may save steps. If you're running a longer program, breaking it into subroutines and then putting it together in one main program can be very helpful. It's a great aid to troubleshooting and debugging if you happen to have a problem, since you can check the function of your program in easy-to-examine "bite-size pieces".

Using subroutines is a convenient way to organize your thinking while programming. By giving subroutines easily defined roles in your program, it's also a lot easier for other programmers to use the programs you write — and to understand your logic in putting the program together.

It's also a good idea, as you become more experienced as a programmmer, to write any and all of your programs so that they can easily be used as subroutines in other programs. This isn't at all difficult to do. In fact, if you just stop the program with an INV SBR instead of an R/S instruction, you can just lift it, label it, and use it as a subroutine where needed. (Note that INV SBR will act just like an R/S instruction if it's not used as part of a subroutine called with the SBR **n** key sequence. If you're just running along in a regular program, and the program pointer "hits" an INV SBR sequence, the program just stops.)

COMBINATIONS:
SBR **AND** INV SBR

Let's consider a program example from statistics that involves the use of subroutines. A "combination" calculation arises when things are being put together in groups (say 10 items grouped 3 at a time without repeating). The general formula for the number of ways n things may be combined, r at a time, is written $\binom{n}{r}$ or $_nC_r$ and equals: $\dfrac{n!}{(n-r)!\,r!}$

(remember that n! means "n factorial" — see *Chapter 4*).

DESTINATION

You want a program that allows you to enter the total number of the things you are looking at (n) and press R/S ; then enter the number you want in each group r, press R/S ; and the calculator will display the number of combinations of n things taken r at a time ($_nC_r$).

PLANNING THE ROUTE

To compute the factorial, we'll use a subroutine that works with the 2nd Dsz key sequence, as we described in *Chapter 4*. We can "lift" the factorial program described in that chapter and use it as a subroutine here, by just starting it with a label, (label 2), and ending it with an INV SBR key sequence.

We'll calculate n!, store it in memory 1; calculate r!, store it in memory 2; calculate (n−r)!, store it in memory 3; then use these results to compute

MAKING TRACKS
$$_nC_r = \frac{n!}{(n-r)!\,r!}$$

Enter the program carefully from the flow chart on the next page.

RUNNING IT

Using your program, calculate the number of poker hands (5 cards) that can be dealt from deck of 52 cards ($_{52}C_5$).

PRESS	DISPLAY/COMMENTS
52 R/S	**8.0658175 67** (This is 52!) *Note:* Allow time for your calculator to finish.
5 R/S	**2598960.** the number of possible poker hands from a 52 card deck ($_{52}C_5$).

Now let's say you would like to use *just* the subroutine part of the program to find 10!

    10 SBR **2**   **3628800.**   (this is 10!)

Note: Our subroutine for factorial gives the incorrect result of 0!=0, instead of 1. For this reason you'll get incorrect results if you use this program in cases where n=r.

MAKING TRACKS

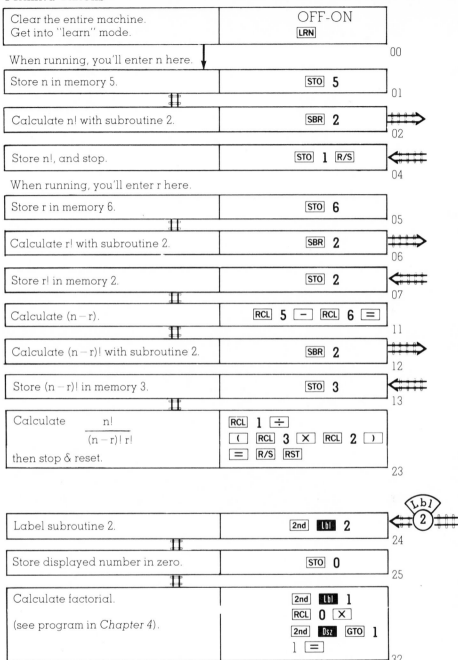

Clear the entire machine. Get into "learn" mode.	OFF-ON [LRN]	
		00

When running, you'll enter n here. ↓

Store n in memory 5.	[STO] **5**	
		01

Calculate n! with subroutine 2.	[SBR] **2**	
		02

Store n!, and stop.	[STO] **1** [R/S]	
		04

When running, you'll enter r here.

Store r in memory 6.	[STO] **6**	
		05

Calculate r! with subroutine 2.	[SBR] **2**	
		06

Store r! in memory 2.	[STO] **2**	
		07

Calculate (n − r).	[RCL] **5** [−] [RCL] **6** [=]	
		11

Calculate (n − r)! with subroutine 2.	[SBR] **2**	
		12

Store (n − r)! in memory 3.	[STO] **3**	
		13

Calculate $\dfrac{n!}{(n-r)!\,r!}$ then stop & reset.	[RCL] **1** [÷] [(] [RCL] **3** [×] [RCL] **2** [)] [=] [R/S] [RST]	
		23

Label subroutine 2.	[2nd] **lbl** **2**	
		24

Store displayed number in zero.	[STO] **0**	
		25

Calculate factorial. (see program in *Chapter 4*).	[2nd] **lbl** **1** [RCL] **0** [×] [2nd] **Dsz** [GTO] **1** **1** [=]	
		32

End of subroutine.	[INV] [SBR]	
		33

Get out of "learn" and reset.	[LRN] [RST]	

COUNTING DOWN! LOOPS WITH [INV] [2nd] [Dsz]

As we move on to some of the more advanced features on your calculator, we'll be covering some of the special uses involving the [2nd] [Dsz] keys. This versatile feature enables loops to be set up and counted in many programming situations. You've already seen in *Chapter 4* how the [2nd] [Dsz] (decrement and skip on zero) key sequence enables simple "lap counting" in a loop situation. The [2nd] [Dsz] key sequence has an *inverse* too, that simply reverses the conditions of the skip. The [INV] [2nd] [Dsz] sequence could be called the "Decrement and Skip if NOT Zero" sequence. When the program pointer encounters this sequence, here's what happens:

[INV] [2nd] [Dsz]

- The calculator subtracts one from whatever (positive integer) is stored in memory zero.
- The calculator then asks, "Is the result equal to zero?"
- If the answer is "yes", go right on to the program step *immediately following* the [Dsz] .
- If the answer is "no", skip right over the following step and on to the next instruction.

Here's a picture of what happens:

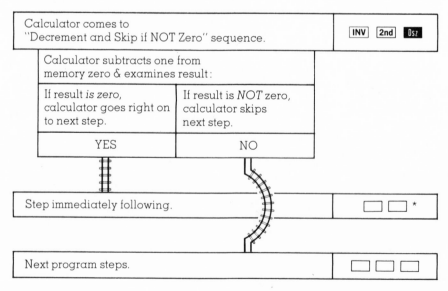

*Note: This step can be anything. However, a [GTO] **n** key sequence is especially useful to move the program pointer to other labelled program points.

The only difference between this *inverse* key sequence and the "regular" [2nd] [Dsz] key sequence is that in this case the calculator will skip most of the time, and only go on to the instruction immediately following when the content of memory zero equals zero. Note that you can follow the [INV] [2nd] [Dsz] key sequence with any program step, but you'll find that following this sequence with a [GTO] n instruction will allow you to easily set up loops. Let's look at a simple example:

DESTINATION

Develop a program that will count *down* from any number you enter in the display. You'd like to enter the number, press [R/S], and have the calculator count down by one from that number to one, then stop.

PLANNING THE ROUTE

Take the displayed number and store it immediately in memory zero. Label that point, and put down the decrement skip if *not* zero sequence. In this case, use a [GTO] immediately following [INV] [2nd] [Dsz] to take you to a point that stops the program. Right after the [INV] [2nd] [Dsz] [GTO] n sequence you want to continue your loop, so recall memory zero, insert two pauses and a [GTO] 1 to count down. Follow the steps in the flow chart.

MAKING TRACKS

Key in the program steps from the *Making Tracks* chart on the next page.

RUNNING IT

At this point, you can count down from any number. Key the program in carefully from the flow chart. Then:

PRESS	DISPLAY/COMMENTS
5	5
[R/S]	4.
	3.
	2.
	1. (Program stops here.)

MAKING TRACKS

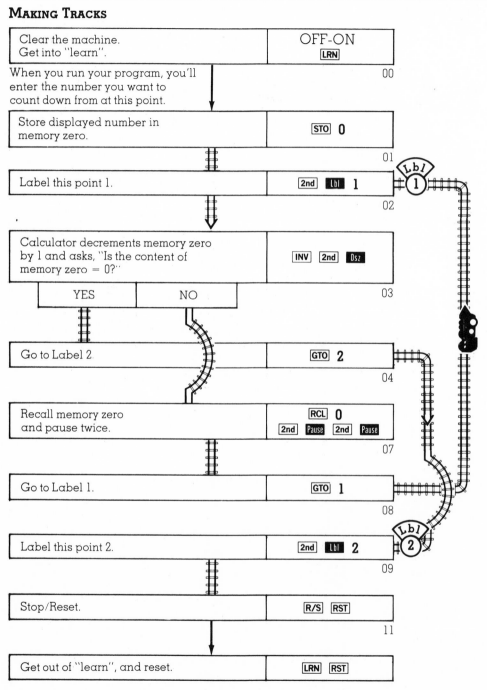

Clear the machine. Get into "learn".	OFF-ON [LRN]

When you run your program, you'll enter the number you want to count down from at this point.

00

Store displayed number in memory zero.	[STO] 0

01

Label this point 1.	[2nd] [Lbl] 1

02

Calculator decrements memory zero by 1 and asks, "Is the content of memory zero = 0?"	[INV] [2nd] [Dsz]

YES	NO

03

Go to Label 2.	[GTO] 2

04

Recall memory zero and pause twice.	[RCL] 0 [2nd] [Pause] [2nd] [Pause]

07

Go to Label 1.	[GTO] 1

08

Label this point 2.	[2nd] [Lbl] 2

09

Stop/Reset.	[R/S] [RST]

11

Get out of "learn", and reset.	[LRN] [RST]

ADDITIONAL FEATURES AND TRICKS WITH [2nd] [Dsz]

The [2nd] [Dsz] key sequence (and its inverse [INV] [2nd] [Dsz]) are powerful programming features of your calculator. You'll be seeing more of the things they can do for you as you proceed through the later sections of this book. Until now, though, we've tried to give you just a first look at the most straightforward applications of these key sequences as "loop counters". At this point, we'd like to go on to show you a bit more on how these key sequences will behave in different situations.

USING [Dsz] WITH NEGATIVE NUMBERS IN MEMORY 0

In our previous examples we've used [2nd] [Dsz] and [INV] [2nd] [Dsz] with *positive integers* in memory 0. However, the [Dsz] feature will also work with *negative numbers* in memory 0. When a negative number is stored in memory zero, the [Dsz] instruction will first *add* 1 to the negative number, then ask if the contents of memory 0 equals zero. The program will then move on, or skip, depending on the result. Using [2nd] [Dsz] with negative numbers gives you an *increment* and skip on 0 operation. To keep things straight, here's a summary of what happens with the [2nd] [Dsz] key sequence, using positive or negative numbers in memory 0.

If the number in memory 0 is *positive*	If the number in memory 0 is *negative*

— When the calculator comes —
to [2nd] [Dsz] in a program

It *subtracts* one from the number in memory 0	It *adds* one to the number in memory 0

— The calculator then asks:
"Is the result equal to 0?"

If *yes*: *Skip* the next instruction
and continue.

If *no* : Go right to the next instruction

Basically, then [2nd] [Dsz] will perform equally well with positive or negative numbers in memory 0 (as will its inverse — the [INV] [2nd] [Dsz] sequence).

USING [2nd] [Dsz] WITH NON-INTEGER NUMBERS IN MEMORY 0:

In all previous examples, we've used *integer* values in memory 0 when we're using [2nd] [Dsz] . However, [2nd] [Dsz] will also operate if the number placed in memory 0 is a non-integer (any number with a whole and decimal part, such as 3.8). If you start with a non-integer number in memory zero, though, you cannot get exactly to "zero" by subtracting 1 from it each time. You need, then, to be aware of exactly what the calculator does when using the [2nd] [Dsz] key sequence with non-integer numbers in memory 0.

Let's say we've entered the number 3.8 in memory 0, and we're running a program that has a [2nd] [Dsz] [GTO] **n** key sequence in it. Here's a chart showing what would happen:

Contents of memory zero when calculator comes to [2nd] [Dsz]	Calculator first subtracts 1 from memory 0	Then calculator asks: "Is content of memory zero equal to zero?"	Program Pointer Will:
1st time 3.8	−1 = 2.8	No	Go to **n**
2nd time 2.8	−1 = 1.8	No	Go to **n**
3rd time 1.8	−1 = .8	No	Go to **n**
4th time 0.8	−1 = 0*	Yes	*Skip*

*When the results of a decrement operation will cause the contents of memory zero to change sign, the calculator just stores a zero in memory zero. Since $0.8 − 1 = −0.2$, the calculator sees the change in sign, automatically loads a zero in memory 0, then skips.

Here's another way to look at this. When a non-integer value is stored in memory 0, the calculator will go through the same number of loops as if the *next larger integer* were stored. Our 3.8 then would produce the same number of loops as a 4; a 4.1 would give you 5; 6.7 would yield 7; − 3.2 the same as − 4; etc.

To see this, let's take a look at a program that shows the [2nd] [Dsz] sequence in operation. This program pauses during each loop to look at the contents of memory 0 *right before* the [2nd] [Dsz] program step. The final display will show the value in memory 0 before the last [Dsz] operation. (a .8 in our 3.8 example). To see the "automatic 0" in memory 0, just push [RCL] **0** after the program halts.

Now, key in this program and then try the examples shown
on the next page.

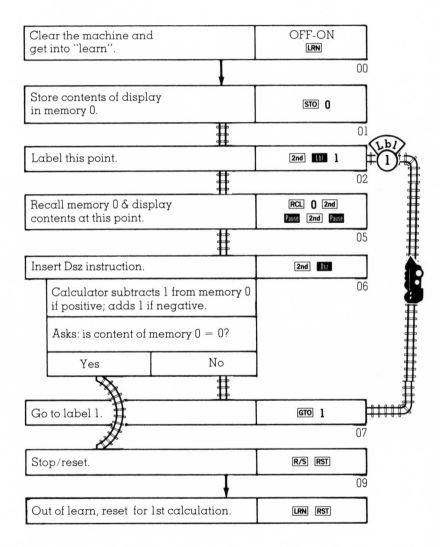

Clear the machine and get into "learn".	OFF-ON [LRN]	
		00
Store contents of display in memory 0.	[STO] 0	
		01
Label this point.	[2nd] [Lbl] 1	
		02
Recall memory 0 & display contents at this point.	[RCL] 0 [2nd] [Pause] [2nd] [Pause]	
		05
Insert Dsz instruction.	[2nd] [Dsz]	
		06

Calculator subtracts 1 from memory 0 if positive; adds 1 if negative.

Asks: is content of memory 0 = 0?

Yes	No

Go to label 1.	[GTO] 1	
		07
Stop/reset.	[R/S] [RST]	
		09
Out of learn, reset for 1st calculation.	[LRN] [RST]	

Now, try these examples:

PRESS	DISPLAY/COMMENTS
4 [+/-] [R/S]	**−4.** Enters negative integer
	−3. [2nd] [Dsz] *adds* 1 each
	−2. loop.
	−1. Stops since value in memory 0 = 0.
[RCL] 0	**0.** A zero in memory 0
3.8 [R/S]	**3.8** Enter positive *non*-integer
	2.8 Calculator *subtracts* 1
	1.8 each loop.
	0.8 Stop since value in memory 0 = 0.
[RCL] 0	**0.** A "0" stored automatically in memory 0 (Notice the 3.8 acted just like a 4)
4.7 [+/-] [R/S]	**−4.7** Enter negative non-integer
	−3.7
	−2.7 Calculator *adds* 1 each loop
	−1.7
	−0.7 Stop since value in memory 0 = 0.
[RCL] 0	**0.** A "0" automatically stored with last [Dsz] operation.

THE TRACKMAKERS: A TOUR OF THE PROGRAMMING KEYS

Your calculator is a powerful problem-solving device, equipped with a variety of features that are ready to use — right from the keyboard. In addition, though, your calculator is programmable. This means you can *teach* your calculator to "push its own buttons" to automatically perform a variety of calculations (including those that involve decisions). You can teach your calculator up to 50 problem-solving steps, and then have it execute these steps as often as you like — with the touch of a single key! If you've just read through the first half of this book, you've already seen programmability in action. If you haven't read this book from the beginning, and if this is your first experience with programming, we encourage you to learn the basics of programming, one step at a time, by reading *Chapters 3* through 6. These chapters are designed to be a short, self-paced course in programming basics. In this chapter we'll go on a tour of the keys on your machine especially devoted to programs and programming. If you already have some programming experience, you may be able to just take this brief tour, pick up your calculator and program it right away. If you've just finished reading *Chapters 3* through 6, this chapter will serve as a quick review.

WHAT'S HAPPENING INSIDE:

The way your calculator "learns" a program is in reality quite simple. There's a special *memory*, called a "program memory" inside your machine, that remembers the program keystrokes you teach it. As you program your machine, each keystroke sequence you enter is stored in order in this memory as a simple code. When you've finished entering a program, your calculator can then go back, read the "codes" in order, and push its own buttons for you in the exact sequence you've taught it.

To enter a program, you use the programming keys clustered on the left side of your keyboard. These keys let you teach the calculator the necessary problem-solving keystrokes. When you've taught your calculator a program, it's as if you've set up "tracks" for it to run on — a path for it to follow in solving your problem. When the calculator is programmed and ready to go, you can start it off at the beginning of these tracks and, much like a train, run down the line of steps you've entered. The "track" is your program — stored in program memory — and the "train" is called the *program pointer*. As the train on the program track comes to (or points to) each step you've programmed, the calculator pushes its own buttons for you as it was directed.

This chapter, then, will give you a quick review of the "trackmakers" — or programming keys of your calculator.

LRN — THE LEARN KEY

Pressing this key once puts your calculator in the "learn" mode of operation — ready to be taught a program. When the calculator is in "learn" mode, the display takes on a whole new format, displaying 4 (and sometimes 5) digits.

00 00

The left two digits in the display will indicate the *step number* you are about to enter into the machine. (You can enter up to 50 steps, labelled 00 through 49.) The digits to the right are for key codes. These are two and three-digit numbers that tell the calculator which program steps you're entering. These right two digits (and a 3rd one that will pop up as you enter certain keystrokes) will be zero *while you enter a program.* This is because the display is always reading out the *step you are ready to enter*, and immediately moves to the next step location in program memory after you enter a step. (Later we'll be discussing how you can go back and check the key codes for each step you've entered.)

Pressing the LRN *key a second time takes your calculator out of "learn" mode*, and it's ready to run a program — or do calculations right from the keyboard. At this point the display changes back to its standard format.

Note that while you're in "learn" mode, the calculator won't do keyboard calculations — it will interpret each keystroke you enter as a program step to be stored. Once you've stored a program and get out of "learn" mode, you can do any keyboard calculations you need to — without affecting the program stored in program memory. Also, note that turning your calculator OFF clears the program memory completely (as well as all other calculator memories and registers).

RST — THE RESET KEY

This is the "start back at the beginning" key. It tells the program pointer to go back to step 00. This key can be used as part of a program (you can enter it while in "learn" mode), or right from the keyboard when out of "learn" mode. When encountered as part of a program, the program pointer immediately jumps back to the very first step — step 00, and keeps on going. When used from the keyboard when *out* of "learn" mode, pressing RST just sets the program pointer to step 00.

The RST also has other special functions. It resets the subroutine level counter back to zero and clears the subroutine return register.

R/S — THE RUN/STOP KEY

Pressing the R/S key (when *out* of "learn" mode) tells your calculator to *start* running a program (from the current location of the program pointer). If a program *is* running, pressing this key (and holding it momentarily) tells it to stop. The R/S key has a dual function — if things are stopped, it starts them going; if a program is running, it stops it.

The R/S key can be used as part of a program, too — when entered *in* "learn" mode. If a program is running and it encounters an R/S instruction as a program step, it simply stops and displays whatever is currently in the display register. This allows you to stop a program to see intermediate results, to enter new numbers the program may need to work on, or to halt the action when the program is finished.

Note that when you're out of "learn" mode and press R/S, the program pointer begins stepping through program memory *starting from its current location*. If you want to start at the first program step (step 00), you need to press RST before pressing R/S. (You can position the program pointer at any other location you'd like to start at with the GTO key — discussed later.)

2nd Pause — THE PAUSE KEY SEQUENCE

This key sequence is designed to be used as part of programs, and you enter it into your program while in "learn" mode. While a program is running and the program pointer comes to a 2nd Pause instruction, it stops the program for about ¾ of a second and displays whatever result is in the display register at that point. Then, it continues on to the next step.

The 2nd Pause key sequence lets you get a quick look at a program result, without stopping the action. This sequence is especially handy when used in repetitive programs (or "loops") — letting you watch the changing results of continuing calculations. You can watch your money "grow" in a compound interest account as the months go by, or watch a function go to a "limit", etc. If you'd like a pause that's *longer* than ¾ of a second, you can just add additional 2nd Pause key sequences, and keep things in the display ¾ of a second longer for each pause sequence you add. (Keep in mind, however, that each 2nd Pause key sequence you add to a program will use up one of your 50 allowed program steps.)

The pause feature can also be used while a program is running by pressing the SST key. This stops the program and displays the result at that point for one pause. If you press and hold the SST key while the program is running you have a "continuous pause" that causes the program to pause one time at each program step. Releasing the key restores normal operation.

2nd Lbl n – THE LABEL KEY SEQUENCE

This key allows you to *label* any point in a program (or an entire program), or a subroutine (subroutines will be discussed later). When in "learn" mode, you press the 2nd Lbl n key sequence, where **n** is any digit **0** through **9**. This lets you label up to 10 points in a program. (Label numbers cannot be repeated in the same programs.)

Labels in a program are convenient, because they work with other keys (GTO and SBR), to let you place the program pointer at any point in a program you select. Labels don't interfere with any program steps or calculations in progress — they are just reference "signposts" for you and the program pointer. You should put a label at any key point in your program — especially if you are going to want the program pointer to go (or "transfer") to that point as your program runs. If you label a program point, you can start your program running from that point easily by using the GTO key (we'll discuss this in a moment).

MERGED CODES:

The entire 2nd Lbl n key sequence takes only one program step, because the calculator stores both the instruction and label digit with a special shortened code called a *merged* code. Try this on your calculator: Turn it OFF and then ON, press LRN , then 2nd Lbl . The display now reads:

00 86 0

The first two digits are the step number: **00**, the next two digits are the code for "label": **86**, and the last digit (zero) is the location for the label number (**0-9**). You would now enter a label digit to complete the label — say **3**. When you press 3 the display reads: **01 00**, which is the next step location for program entry.

There are several program key sequences that use this merged code format. Basically, these are any of the functions that require a label number or memory location to be complete. (All the memory instructions STO RCL , etc. are examples.) Whenever you see the third rightmost digit light up while you're programming in "learn" mode, the calculator is requesting a label or memory number (0-9). (Don't forget to put one in — and, also, keep a record of what each label or memory is being used for.) Note that the 2nd FIX n key sequence also uses a merged code.

7

THE TRACKMAKERS

GTO n — THE "GO TO"
KEY SEQUENCE
GTO 2nd nn — THE
"GO TO A STEP NUMBER"
KEY SEQUENCE

GTO n – THE "GO TO" KEY SEQUENCE

This key sequence can be used as part of a program (when entered *in* "learn" mode), or right off the keyboard (when *out* of "learn" mode). Pressing GTO **n**, where **n** is a *label number* (**0** through **9**) immediately moves the program pointer to the label number **n**. In a program, when the program pointer encounters a GTO **n** instruction, it goes right to label **n**, and continues on from that point. (The GTO **n** sequence is stored as one program step — with a "merged" code.)

The GTO key creates what is called an "unconditional transfer" when you use it in a program. No matter what's going on, when the program pointer comes to a GTO **n**, it goes right to the program label **n** and continues running. There are other types of program transfers made possible by combining the GTO **n** key sequence with other keys. These other keys let you place a *condition* right before the GTO **n** instruction. When you use these other keys (discussed in *Chapter 6* and reviewed later), you can build decision points into your program — and create what are called *conditional transfers*.

The GTO **n** sequence is handy in a variety of situations. You can, for example, write a long program that performs several different functions. If you *label* each function with its own label number, you can easily use each function individually — without running the entire program. When *out* of "learn" mode just press GTO **n** (the label number of the function you want), and then start the program with the R/S key. The program pointer will start up from the labeled point.

GTO 2nd nn – THE "GO TO A STEP NUMBER" KEY SEQUENCE

This key sequence can be used only when *out* of "learn" mode. It simply lets you position the program pointer at any step number you choose. When out of "learn" mode, if you press GTO 2nd , and then any two digit program step number (00-49), the program pointer immediately moves to that step number. This feature is especially handy if you want to change or correct a program step (see editing keys — discussed later); or if you'd like to start the program pointer from some unlabeled point in a program.

Try this on your calculator. Turn it OFF, then ON, and press GTO 2nd **16**. Now press LRN . The display reads **16 00**, telling you that you've moved the program pointer to step location 16. In similar fashion you could locate the program pointer at any step: 0 through 49. (Trying to go beyond step 49 results in a flashing error indication).

[2nd] [Dsz] — The "Decrement and Skip on Zero" Key Sequence

This key sequence is a powerful one. It lets you set up a repetitive calculation (or "loop") for as many times as you select. (You store the number of repetitions in memory zero). What this sequence really does is allow you to control whether or not the program pointer moves on to the step that immediately follows it, or *skips* that step and goes on to the next one. When the program pointer comes to a [2nd] [Dsz] key sequence in a program here's what happens:

- First, the contents of memory zero are decreased by one. (This assumes that a positive integer is in memory 0. If a *fractional* number is in memory zero, the calculator "acts" as if the *next* larger number is in memory zero. If a *negative* number is in memory zero, it is incremented by one.)
- The calculator then asks: is the content of memory zero *equal* to zero?
- If the answer is *no*, the program pointer proceeds right on to the step following [2nd] [Dsz] .
- If the answer is *yes*, the program pointer *skips the following* instruction and continues.

The step that immediately follows the [2nd] [Dsz] key sequence can be anything, but a [GTO] **n** instruction is often handy at this point for setting up repetitive calculations. For example, in the program situation shown in the diagram, the "series of program instructions" would be executed repetitively because of the loop.

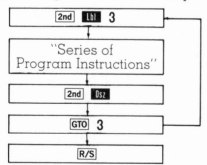

The number of *times* the "instructions" were executed would be controlled by the number stored in memory zero (stored before running the program). If a 6 were stored in memory zero, the series of instructions would be carried out 6 times, then the program would halt.

Note that the series of instructions would also be executed 6 times if a 5.2, a −6, or a −5.2 were stored in memory zero before the program pointer arrived at this series of instructions. Also, be aware of the fact that since memory zero is involved whenever [2nd] [Dsz] is used, it cannot be used for other storage purposes while handling a [2nd] [Dsz] sequence, although the number in memory 0 can be used as part of the computational sequence by recalling it.

INV 2nd Dsz — The "Decrement and Skip If Not Zero" Key Sequence

This key sequence works in the same fashion as the previous one, except the condition of the skip is reversed. When the program pointer comes to an INV 2nd Dsz key sequence, here's what happens:

- One is subtracted from the contents of memory zero. (Again, it's assumed that the number in memory zero is a positive integer. If it's fractional, it acts as if the *next* largest integer is in memory zero. If the number in memory zero is negative, one is *added* to it.)
- The calculator then asks, is the content of memory *zero equal to* zero?
- If the answer is *no*, the program pointer *skips* the instruction immediately following the INV 2nd Dsz sequence.
- If the answer is *yes*, the program pointer proceeds right on to the instruction immediately following the INV 2nd Dsz .

This instruction is also handy for setting up repetitive calculations in a variety of programing situations.

For additional details on the 2nd Dsz and INV 2nd Dsz key sequences and their use, see *Chapters 4* and *6*.

CONDITIONAL TRANSFERS

There is a family of instructions on your calculator designed to let you build decision-making into your programs. The basic operation of this family of instructions is similar — and they're quite easy to learn, but they are also flexible enough to allow a great deal of programming power.

Basically when a *conditional transfer* key sequence is encountered in a program, the calculator immediately compares two quantities: the number in the display register (called x) and the number in a special test or "t" register (called t). (The "t" or test register is just memory 7 on your calculator.) The calculator then asks one of 4 questions about how x and t compare — depending on the program instruction you use:

[2nd] [x=t]	Is x = t? (Is x equal t?)
[INV] [2nd] [x=t]	Is x ≠ t? (Is x not equal t?)
[2nd] [x≥t]	Is x ≥ t? (Is x greater than or equal to t?)
[INV] [2nd] [x≥t]	Is x < t? (Is x less than t?)

If the answer is yes, the program pointer goes on to the instruction immediately following. If the answer is NO, the program pointer SKIPS the instruction immediately following and continues.

Let's go through each of the conditional transfer instructions (and the keys for using them) one at a time.

[x⇄t] — THE "x EXCHANGE WITH t" KEY

When this key is pressed the contents of the display register and the "t" register (memory 7) are just exchanged. This provides a convenient method of getting any test, or t, value into the test register. (You can also use the [2nd] [Exc] 7 key sequence, or simply the [STO] 7 sequence if it is appropriate in your program.)

[2nd] [x=t] — THE "Is x EQUAL TO t?" KEY SEQUENCE

You can enter this key sequence while in "learn" mode to have the program pointer take one of several pathways in your program. When the program pointer comes to this instruction in a program, the calculator compares what's in the display register (x) and what's in the "t" register (t) and asks: Is x equal to t? If the answer is *yes*, the calculator goes right on to the step following the [2nd] [x=t] key sequence. If *no*, the pointer *skips* whatever instruction follows and moves on to the next instruction and continues.

The instruction that immediately follows the [2nd] [x=t] key sequence can be anything, but you'll find a [GTO] n key sequence especially useful, as shown in the diagram below:

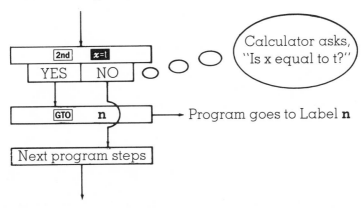

Again, key things to remember when using the [2nd] [x=t] key sequence:
- The calculator asks the question: Is x = t?
- If the answer is *yes* — it goes on to the step immediately following.
- If the answer is *no* — it *SKIPS* the step following and goes on.

OTHER CONDITIONAL TRANSFERS:

[INV] [2nd] [x=t] — "Is x Not Equal to t?" (x ≠ t) Key Sequence

This key sequence is entered into a program (while in "learn" mode) to create a conditional program transfer (or decision). When the program pointer encounters the "Is x *not* equal to t?" key sequence — [INV] [2nd] [x=t] — the following things happen:
- The calculator compares the contents of the display register (x) to the contents of the test register (register 7).
- The calculator asks: Is x *not* equal (or unequal) to t?
- If the answer is *yes*, the program pointer *goes right on* to the step that immediately follows.
- If the answer is *no*, the program pointer *SKIPS* the following step and continues.

Again note that the program step immediately following the [INV] [2nd] [x=t] key sequence can be any program step you choose, though a [GTO] n is especially handy at these points.

2nd x≥t — "Is x GREATER THAN OR EQUAL TO t?" KEY SEQUENCE

When the program pointer comes to this instruction in a program, the following things happen:

- The calculator compares the contents of the x and t registers.
- It asks the question: "Is x greater than or equal to t?"
- If the answer is *yes,* it goes on to the instruction that immediately follows.
- If the answer is *no,* it *skips* the following instruction and continues.

INV 2nd x≥t — "Is x LESS THAN t?" — (x<t) KEY SEQUENCE

When the program pointer comes to this instruction in a program, the following things happen:

- The calculator compares the contents of the x and t registers.
- It asks the question: "Is x less than t?"
- If the answer is *yes,* it goes *on* to the step immediately following the INV 2nd x≥t key sequence.
- If the answer is *no,* it *skips* the step immediately following, and continues.

ADDITIONAL NOTES:

It's really quite easy to remember these instructions if you keep your eye on the "big picture". Basically you can have the calculator make any one of four tests: Is x equal t, is x greater than or equal t, or their inverses — Is x unequal t, Is x less than t? Whatever the case, the calculator makes a test and asks a question. If the answer to the question is *yes,* it goes right on to the step immediately following. If the answer is *no,* it *skips* the step immediately following, and continues.

Note that the quantity x that's compared to t is the *contents of the display register.* The display register holds numbers to 11 digits, of which only 8 are actually shown (correctly rounded) in the calculator's display window. In certain cases these last 3 digits can affect the outcome of the comparisons described in this section. (These cases are rare, but if a problem should arise, it's helpful to know about this possibility.) One way to avoid problems with the last 3 digits (called guard digits) is to use the key sequence EE   INV   EE . This key sequence will truncate the 3 guard digits of a result leaving only the rounded display value for further use (see Appendix D). For additional details on the use of these key sequences, as well as sample programs using them, refer to *Chapter 6.*

SUBROUTINES

Using subroutines is not only a handy technique for saving program steps and breaking a large program down into easy to analyze segments: it's also just plain good programming practice. A subroutine is just a "miniprogram" you can write as part of any program. Anytime you need to use a set of program steps more than once in a program, it's a good idea to make that series of steps into a subroutine. Here's how:

To make any series of program steps into a subroutine, all you need to do is:
   •Start the series of program steps with a *Label*.
   •End the series of steps with an INV SBR key sequence.

Subroutines can be of any length, as long as your entire program with all its subroutines is no more than 50 steps.

To Use a Subroutine in a Program:
   •While in "learn" mode, anytime you need to use any subroutine, just press: SBR **n,** where n is the label of the subroutine. You can use (or "call", as is sometimes said) a subroutine as many times as you'd like in a program.

When the program pointer comes to a SBR **n** key sequence in a program, the calculator does the following things for you (illustrated in the diagram):

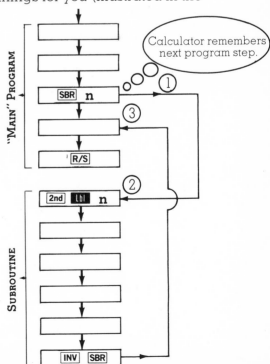

Calculator remembers next program step.

① First, it "notes" the step in the program where the SBR **n** instruction occurs in a special memory (called the subroutine return memory).

② The program pointer goes right to label **n** and starts executing the instructions after it, until it comes to the INV SBR instruction.

③ When the program pointer reaches the INV SBR instruction, it returns to the point where the subroutine was "called", and continues.

THE TRACKMAKERS **7**

To Use Subroutines Right from the Keyboard:

One advantage of using subroutines in a program is that you can use any subroutine in the program separately from the program itself. To do this, just press [SBR] **n** while *out* of "learn" mode. The program pointer will immediately go to label **n** and execute the subroutine. In this case the [INV] [SBR] key sequence at the end of the subroutine will act just like an [R/S] instruction.

Notes on Subroutines:

Using subroutines is *good programming practice!* Subroutines let you organize your programs easily (and thus can help you find errors — if they exist.) It's also easier for other programmers to understand and use your programs when they're in bite-size subroutine "chunks".

Your calculator is equipped with *two levels* of subroutine capability. This means that while you're inside one subroutine, you can "call" or use another subroutine. You can't go to a third level, however. If a second level subroutine tries to "call" a third, a flashing error condition will be created. The "subroutine return" memory has room for only two return locations.

You can easily write any of your programs so that they can be used as subroutines in other programs. (In fact, most experienced programmers suggest that you do this.) Naturally, this won't be practical for programs that contain close to 50 steps — but it's a good procedure to follow for any shorter programs. To do this, just start the program with a label, and end it with an [INV] [SBR] key sequence. The [INV] [SBR] key sequence acts just like an [R/S] instruction if the subroutine return memory is empty.

PROGRAM EDITING: KEY CODES

Your calculator is equipped with a series of keys that allow you to alter your programs easily and rapidly to fit new problem solving situations, or to correct any errors you may have in your program. These *editing* features of the calculator let you get to any point in a program, analyze it, change a step, add or delete steps, or leave "blanks" in the program for later use.

As was mentioned earlier in this chapter, your calculator stores the steps in any program as a sequence of key codes. These codes are arrived at in a pretty straightforward fashion. The code for any *number* key on the keyboard is just the number itself (00 through 09). The key code for any first function key is a two digit number: The first digit is the row the key is in, the second digit is its column. (Rows are numbered from 1 to 8 top to bottom, columns from 1 to 5 left to right, as shown in the diagram.)

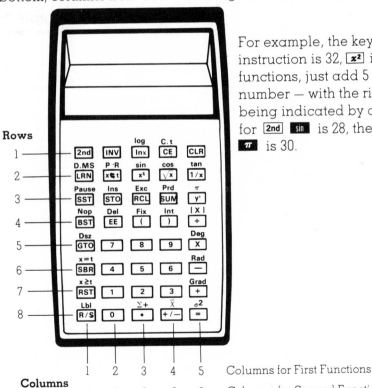

For example, the key code for the STO instruction is 32, x² is 23. For second functions, just add 5 to the column number — with the rightmost column being indicated by a zero. The code for 2nd sin is 28, the code for 2nd π is 30.

Rows

1
2
3
4
5
6
7
8

1 2 3 4 5   Columns for First Functions
Columns
6 7 8 9 0   Columns for Second Functions

When you first enter a program in "learn" mode, you won't see the key codes, because the program memory display always moves ahead to the next step. To see the codes in any program, you need to enter the program first, then go back and examine the codes. Here's how to do this:

Let's enter a simple program to work with. We'll enter a program that displays the *squares* of the counting numbers (1, 2, 3, ... etc.) Key in the program as follows:

PRESS	DISPLAY/COMMENTS
OFF-ON	**0** Clears entire machine
LRN	**00 00**
1	**01 00**
SUM	**01 34 0**
2	**02 00**
RCL	**02 33 0**
2	**03 00**
x^2	**04 00**
2nd Pause	**05 00**
RST	**06 00**
LRN RST	**0**

To run this program, just press R/S and you should see 1, 4, 9, 16, etc. Press R/S and hold it momentarily to stop the program. Now, using this program you can check on the key codes and edit, using the keys and features described on this and the following page. (Press RST now to get back to the beginning of the program.)

SST – SINGLE STEP KEY

When used in "learn" mode, this key steps through your program one step at a time, and lets you check codes. Note that this key has *no* keycode of its own, and can't be entered as a program step. This key can also be used when *out* of "learn" mode, to *execute* a program one step at a time. For editing you press SST repeatedly, to see the codes for your program:

PRESS	DISPLAY/COMMENTS	
LRN	**00 01**	1
SST	**01 34 2**	SUM 2
SST	**02 33 2**	RCL 2
SST	**03 23**	x^2
SST	**04 36**	2nd Pause
SST	**05 71**	Last program step RST
SST	**06 00**	

[BST] — The Backstep Key

This key operates in "learn" mode only, and lets you step *back* through your program one step at a time. Press [BST] repeatedly to go back through your program codes. (This key also has no code of its own and can't be entered as a program step.)

[GTO] [2nd] **nn**

As was already mentioned, this key sequence can be used when **out** of "learn" mode to go directly to any program step. Press [LRN] to get out of "learn" mode, then press [GTO] [2nd] **05.** Then press [LRN] again. The display shows **05 71** — you're at step 5 in the program which is the [RST] instruction.

To Change or Edit a Program:

You can write over program steps, blank out program steps, insert steps or delete steps. Let's take a quick look at each of these:

To Write Over a Program Step:

Just get to the exact step you want to write over, and simply enter the new keystroke or keystroke sequence. The new instruction will write over the old one and replace it. (The display will move on to the next step as soon as you do this, so you can go back and check the new code with the [BST] key.)

[2nd] [Nop] — The "No Operation or NO-OP" Key Sequence

This sequence lets you blank out any instruction in your program with a "NO-OP" instruction that's simply ignored by the calculator. The [2nd] [Nop] key sequence lets you leave blank spaces in a program you can fill in later, or lets you "blank out" any instruction you wish. Just step to the instruction you want to blank out while in "learn" mode, and press [2nd] [Nop]. A NO-OP instruction (code 46) will replace the old one.

[2nd] [Ins] — "Insert" Key Sequence

This sequence allows you to insert additional steps in a program easily. If you want to add instructions to your program, step to the program step that's right at the point you'd like to add additional steps (while in "learn" mode).

Then press [2nd] [Ins].
This moves all instructions from that point on down by one location, and leaves a blank space at the location you're at. Now you can add a new instruction. To add more instructions, just repeat the process. *Note:* Any step at location 49 will be "pushed off" and lost when you press [2nd] [Ins].

2nd Del — "Delete" Key Sequence

This sequence allows you to remove an instruction from a program, and close up the gap — moving all the following instructions up by one location. Just step to the exact instruction you want to delete, and press the 2nd Del key sequence.

For additional details on editing and key codes, as well as examples, of the editing keys in action, see *Chapter 5*.

Steps in Writing a Program:

As you learn more about programming, you'll begin falling into a "natural rhythm" where programming solutions will begin to suggest themselves to you as soon as you're confronted with a problem. The actual steps you'll follow in getting to a program solution will naturally depend on your personal approach, but these steps suggest one way to proceed:

1. Study the problem — gather the equations and procedures you'll need.
2. Set a destination for yourself. Determine how you'll use the program, so that when the program is complete, you'll know what to enter, what keys you'll press, and what you want to see displayed.
3. *Plan the Program "Route"* — Conceptualize how the program pointer will "flow" through the program (a flow chart or schematic diagram of the steps you'll follow may be helpful here).
4. Write down the actual program steps (or, as you gain confidence, key them right into your machine). As you go along keep careful track of what is stored in each memory, and what any label you use signifies. These are items that are easy to forget, and forgetting them is a common source of error and "start overs".
5. Once the program is entered, check it with known test data to be sure it's working.
6. Edit and correct as necessary.
7. Document or "write up" the program carefully to save it for future use. Standard program record forms are provided for this purpose and the form is arranged to follow the "steps in writing a program" that we've discussed here. Once your program is working, you can press RST , LRN and then use the SST key to step through the key codes and record them on the program record form. This type of complete record will let you (or a friend) pick up the form at a future date and understand the program — how it works, how to use it, *and* how to check it to be certain it's working.

DEVELOPMENT OF PROGRAMMING STYLE:

Whether you're programming your calculator, or a large scale computer — keep one point in mind: there is no single unique programming solution to any problem. As you gain experience in programming, you'll find yourself developing your own unique style, "tricks of the trade", and favorite techniques in getting at a solution. As you begin gaining experience, it's a good idea to review your techniques periodically to be sure you're using all the power of your machine. Don't be afraid to explore new routes, try new alternatives, and experiment with new methods. Programming is an excellent exercise in clear, common sense, logical thinking that many folks enjoy (and some are quite addicted to). Your calculator is deliberately designed to allow you to get started easily, and then grow quite quickly into an expert in creating programs.

MOVING ON:

One more point — your calculator is easy to use, and readily accessible and affordable. *But*, it incorporates *most all of the major features and functions of any large scale computer!* The concepts of a program memory, a program pointer that moves through it, labels, go to instructions, loops and conditional transfers are common to all digital programmable devices. Once you've learned to program your calculator you'll find it quite easy to move on to programming any machine — no matter what the scale. Larger scale computers simply accept their input in different ways, have more ways to get output results to you, and in general are equipped to handle and store larger amounts of information. Most commonly a beginner will approach these machines by writing instructions one at a time, on cards, paper tape or magnetic discs. These one-at-a-time instructions will resemble your keystroke instructions — particularly in most common beginning computer languages such as FORTRAN or BASIC. The keyboard design of your calculator will allow you to learn programming easily in either of these languages, after learning the basics on your machine.

In the next decade, logic and memory will become omnipresent in our everyday lives. Programmable devices will be everywhere — in the kitchen, in your home finances, in communications, in personal security — everywhere. Learning the basics of programming on your calculator *now* will prepare you for the sound use of these devices — and enable you to enjoy them as a *natural* part of your daily living.

CASH TRACKS:
AN INTRODUCTION

At this point, you've seen the basics on *how* to operate your programmable calculator. This chapter, and those that follow, go on to give you a selection of examples that illustrate *where* your programmable will come in especially handy. Bear in mind that these few examples are only a beginning. Keep your imagination "open" as we go through each one. Building *your own* programs and finding new applications for your calculator are an important part of your growth in learning about programming.

As you go through these programs, take the time to follow the flow charts carefully to observe the programming techniques utilized. If you have any difficulties, carefully check each program step for any problems. To help you avoid "keying in" errors, we've included step counter numbers to the right of the blocks on the flow charts. These are the step numbers shown as you are *first keying in* the program. Use these as a guide to avoid "forgetting" where you are.

Calculators are very handy to have while handling "around the house" situations involving numbers and mathematics. They bring a speed and accuracy to calculations that can give you "the edge" in getting best buys, making sound investments, and getting the most out of your money. *Programmable* calculators bring an added dimension to your problem solving capabilities. Whole sequences of keystrokes can be "boiled down" to a single "enter and press" sequence. This lets you "try things out", plan, and watch things happen on your calculator to a degree never before possible. Examples in this chapter include such topic areas as:

•**Comparative Shopping** — Which size package is the best buy? This program not only helps decide which is the best buy, it automatically gives the percent difference.

•**Bank Book Balance** — Ever have problems balancing your checkbook? This program helps check on all the "ins and outs".

•**Bit by Bit** — Do you make regular payments to a savings account? If so, how much money do you have now . . . how much will you have several years from now? This program helps you to find out.

•**Kilowatt Cost** — Ever wonder how much it costs to run your TV set for a month? What happens to your electric bill when someone leaves that basement light on all night? This program can help you find the cost of running any electrical item around the house.

•**Car Fever** — Need to shop around on interest? . . . or do you want to figure out what your monthly payment will be *before* you take out a loan? Here's how.

•**Interesting Points on Interest** — This is a brief (but important) discussion of the method used to relate monthly interest to annual interest, vice versa, and more.

COMPARATIVE SHOPPING

One way to determine which of two similar items is really the better buy (and get the most for your money) is to compare their *unit prices* — *the price of one unit* of each of the items (for example, cost per pound, oz., qt., etc.). The item with the *lowest* unit price is the most economical.

DESTINATION

We'll work up a program that lets you enter the price and quantity (ozs., qts., etc.) of the first item (pressing R/S after each), and then the price and quantity of item 2 the same way. The calculator will then pause to display "1" if item 1 has the lower cost/unit (or "2" if item 2 is lower). After the pause, the calculator calculates and displays the percent difference between the two unit prices.

PLANNING THE ROUTE

Your program should first take the total price of item 1 (entered from the keyboard) and divide it by the number of units. This value should then be stored for comparison with item 2. The unit cost of item 2 should be calculated and stored the same way (in memory 2). After calculating and storing these unit costs, the calculator can compare them using the 2nd x≥t key sequence with 0 in the "t" register. To do this, the unit cost of item 1 is subtracted from the unit cost of item 2 and the difference compared to "t". If the difference is negative, item 1 is cheaper; if the difference is positive, then item 2 is cheaper. The 2nd x≥t key sequence can be set up to display a 1 or 2 to show which is better. Then the percentage difference can be calculated using this formula:

$$\% \text{ difference } = \frac{\text{Higher Unit Cost} - \text{Lower Unit Cost}}{\text{Lower Unit Cost}} \times 100$$

MAKING TRACKS

Enter the program from the flow chart on the following page.

RUNNING IT

Item 1 costs $1.09 for 16 oz. Item 2 costs $0.89 for 12 oz. Which is the better buy and by what percentage?

PRESS	DISPLAY/COMMENTS	
2nd FIX 2	0.00	Fix display at "dollars & cents"
1.09 R/S	1.09	Item 1 price.
16 R/S	0.07	Unit price Item 1.
0.89 R/S	0.89	Item 2 price.
12 R/S	1	Calculator displays a one. (Item 1 is the better buy.)
	8.87	Then displays percent difference.

MAKING TRACKS

Clear and enter "learn".	OFF-ON `LRN`

When you run this program, you'll
enter item 1 price at this point.

Get set to divide.	`÷` `R/S`	02

You'll enter # of units (item 1).

Compute & store item 1's cost/unit.	`=` `STO` 1 `R/S`	05

Enter item 2 price.

Get set to divide.	`÷` `R/S`	07

Enter # of units (item 2).

Compute & store cost/unit (item 2) and find the difference in unit costs.	`=` `STO` 2 `RCL` 1 `−` `RCL` 2 `=`	13

Is difference between unit price positive?	`2nd` `x≥t`	14

YES	NO

If YES, then results are positive — go to label 0.	`GTO` 0	

If NO, results are negative. Item 1 costs less, so display "1".	1 `2nd` `Pause` `2nd` `Pause`	18

Calculate % difference (item 2 larger) & stop, display results, and reset.	`RCL` 2 `−` `RCL` 1 `=` `÷` `RCL` 1 `×` 100 `=` `R/S` `RST`	31

Label for item 2 — best buy.	`2nd` `Lbl` 0	

Item 2 costs less, so display a 2.	2 `2nd` `Pause` `2nd` `Pause`	35

Calculate % difference (item 1 larger) & stop, display result, and reset.	`RCL` 1 `−` `RCL` 2 `=` `÷` `RCL` 2 `×` 100 `=` `R/S` `RST`	48

Get out of "learn" & reset.	`LRN` `RST`

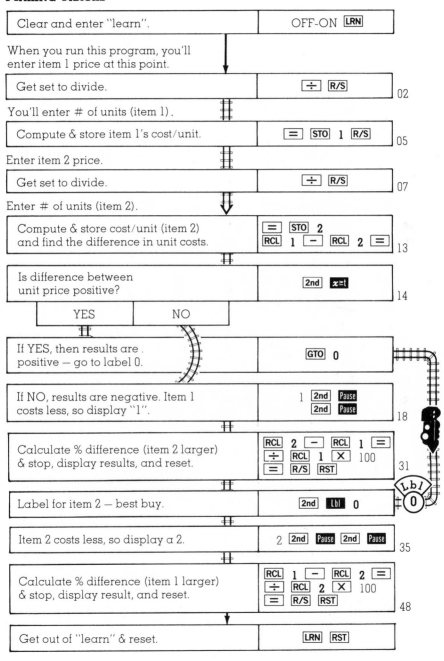

BANK BOOK BALANCE

Once each month all of us have the opportunity to tackle "balancing" our checkbook against our bank statement. Normally, your checkbook balance will not agree with the balance shown on the bank statement because you need to allow for the checks and deposits that haven't cleared yet. But which one do you add . . . ? or do you subtract . . . ? or . . .? Well, in this example we'll develop a program that will help you balance your checkbook.

DESTINATION

We'll design a program that lets you do the following:
- First, you enter the balance from your bank statement and push R/S .
- Then, enter the amounts of your outstanding (uncleared) checks one at a time, pushing R/S after each. When you're finished entering uncleared checks, enter a zero, press R/S and go on.
- Next, enter each outstanding deposit (not shown on your bank statement) one at a time, pressing R/S after each.
- When you're through entering deposits, enter a zero, press R/S and the calculator will display the corrected balance for you to verify with your checkbook balance.
- If these balances don't agree, you can enter the balance you show in your checkbook, push R/S , and the amount you need to add or subtract from your checkbook balance to correct it will be displayed.

PLANNING THE ROUTE

Start by storing the bank statement balance in memory 1. Then, set up a loop using INV SUM 1 to subtract outstanding checks from the balance. An INV 2nd x≷t comparison in this loop can be used so that when you're through entering checks, entering a 0 will get you out of the loop. A similar loop is then used to add deposits to the balance. After the last deposit, the contents of memory 1 should agree with the balance you show in your checkbook. If it doesn't, you can then enter your checkbook balance, take the difference, and the display will show the amount to use to correct your checkbook balance.

MAKING TRACKS

Key in the program from the *Making Tracks* chart on the next page.

Making Tracks

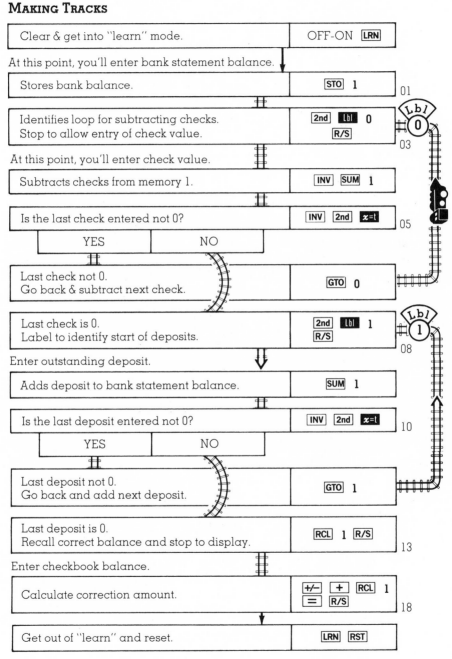

Clear & get into "learn" mode.	OFF-ON [LRN]

At this point, you'll enter bank statement balance.

Stores bank balance.	[STO] 1	01

Identifies loop for subtracting checks. Stop to allow entry of check value.	[2nd] [Lbl] 0 [R/S]	03

At this point, you'll enter check value.

Subtracts checks from memory 1.	[INV] [SUM] 1

Is the last check entered not 0?	[INV] [2nd] [x=t]	05

YES	NO

Last check not 0. Go back & subtract next check.	[GTO] 0

Last check is 0. Label to identify start of deposits.	[2nd] [Lbl] 1 [R/S]	08

Enter outstanding deposit.

Adds deposit to bank statement balance.	[SUM] 1

Is the last deposit entered not 0?	[INV] [2nd] [x=t]	10

YES	NO

Last deposit not 0. Go back and add next deposit.	[GTO] 1

Last deposit is 0. Recall correct balance and stop to display.	[RCL] 1 [R/S]	13

Enter checkbook balance.

Calculate correction amount.	[+/-] [+] [RCL] 1 [=] [R/S]	18

Get out of "learn" and reset.	[LRN] [RST]

RUNNING IT

Your bank statement balance is $940.26. You have outstanding checks of:
$76.83, $122.87, $219.50, $397.31, $231.00, and $138.25. You also have a
$450.00 deposit outstanding. After subtracting your service charge, your
checkbook balance is $209.15. Is this correct?

PRESS	DISPLAY/COMMENTS
940.26 [RST] [R/S]	**940.26** Bank balance.
76.83 [R/S] , 122.87 [R/S] ,	Each amount will show as
219.50 [R/S] , 397.31 [R/S] ,	entered.
231.00 [R/S] , 138.25 [R/S]	
0 [R/S]	**0.** Tells all checks entered.
450 [R/S]	**450.** Deposit.
0 [R/S]	You enter zero to indicate last deposit.
	204.5 Correct balance. Let's say your checkbook record shows a balance of 209.15
209.15 [R/S]	**−4.65** The amount to subtract from your checkbook record to correct your balance.

8

BIT BY BIT: BUILDING A SAVINGS PLAN

A savings account can be an important tool in building a "nest egg". You may just put a lump of money in savings and let it grow. More often, though, you try to save a little at a time with a monthly savings plan. With your programmable calculator, it's easy to set things up so that you can watch how your money will grow with a monthly savings plan.

DESTINATION

We'll develop a program that lets you watch the future value (FV) of your money grow in a monthly savings plan situation. The program will evaluate the formula:

$$FV = PMT \times \left(\frac{((1 + i)^n - 1)}{i} \right)$$

where PMT is your regular savings amount, and i is the decimal value of interest earned for the time interval, n. (Note that this formula does not include interest on partial periods. If you're making deposits once a month, for example, and you deposit on the 20th, interest won't be calculated until the 1st of the month.)

To use this program you'd like to be able to:
- Enter the payment amount, and press [R/S] .
- Enter the decimal interest rate per time period, press [R/S] again, and . . .
- You'd like your calculator to then display the future value of your money (FV) for successive time periods (n = 1, 2, 3, ... etc.), along with the total interest amount you've earned at that point.

PLANNING THE ROUTE

First, store the payment amount in memory 1, and then store the interest rate in memory 2. Then start a loop (at label 0) that will add 1 to memory 3, recall this, and pause to display it. (This generates, increments, and displays n — the period number — for each time around the loop.) Then evaluate the formula

$$FV = PMT \times \left(\frac{((1 + i)^n - 1)}{i} \right)$$, and pause to display FV. To display the

interest earned, subtract the total amount of payments so far (PMT × n) from FV, and pause. Then, loop back to the beginning of the program and continue for the next time period.

MAKING TRACKS

Key in the program from the *Making Tracks* chart on the next page.

RUNNING IT

As an example, assume that your savings account pays 0.7% interest per month, and you're saving $55.00 per month. Let's use our program to watch this account grow for 12 months. Then, calculate the future value (FV) at 60 months.

PRESS	DISPLAY/COMMENTS
55 [R/S]	**55.00** PMT amount.
0.007 [R/S]	**1.00** 1st month.
	55.00 FV = 1st PMT (no interest).
	−0.00 No interest so far.
	2.00
	110.39 2 PMTS + interest .
	0.39 earned interest.
	⋮
	12.00 n = 12.
	686.01 12 PMTS + interest.
	26.01 earned interest.
Press & hold [R/S] to stop	Stops program.
[CLR]	**0** In case you stopped in the middle of a calculation.
59 [STO] 3	**59.00** Stores n − 1 in memory 3 to look at n = 60. (Store n − 1 because program adds 1 to n.)
[GTO] 0 [R/S] (or [SBR] 0)	Goes to start of loop.
	60.00 60th month.
	4083.64 60 PMTS + interest.
	783.64 Earned interest.

Making Tracks

Clear and get into "learn".	OFF-ON LRN

At this point, you'll enter PMT amt.

Store PMT in memory 1.	STO 1 R/S	02

Enter decimal interest rate.

Store i in memory 2, clear memory 3 for n = 0.	STO 2 0 STO 3	05

Identify start of loop.	2nd Lbl 0	06

Generate value of n and pause.	1 SUM 3 RCL 3 2nd Pause 2nd Pause	11

Evaluate FV, store in memory 4, (since you'll need it again to find interest) and pause.	RCL 1 X ((1 + RCL 2) y^x RCL 3 − 1) ÷ RCL 2 = 2nd Pause 2nd Pause	29

Subtracts total PMTS made (PMT × n) from FV to calculate interest earned.	− RCL 1 X RCL 3 = 2nd Pause 2nd Pause	36

Go to 0 and repeat loop.	GTO 0	37

Come out of "learn", reset for running & fix decimal at 2.	LRN RST 2nd FIX 2

Lbl
0

KILOWATT COST

Did you ever wonder how much you're paying each month to use your lights? . . . your TV set? . . . your electric fan? . . . other appliances? This program computes the cost of operation for electrical appliances around your house. All you'll need is your electric bill for last month (since rates fluctuate for different areas and different total usage), and the wattage rating of each item you want to check. (You can find this either printed on the device directly in watts or you can approximate it by multiplying the current (amps) used by the device times the line voltage (115 in U.S.).

DESTINATION

Since you want to know what it costs to run an appliance for a month, you need a program that will calculate the cost per kilowatt-hour (kWh) from your light bill and use this to determine the cost of using any appliance for a month. To do this you'll need to:

•Enter the cost of last month's electric bill (push R/S).
•Enter the kilowatt-hours used from your electric bill (push R/S).
•Enter the number of watts used by the appliance you're testing (push R/S). (If the appliance shows only "amps", enter amps X 115 =, then push R/S .)
•Enter the number of hours you use the appliance per day (push R/S), and then the cost to run this appliance will be displayed.

The program we'll develop will also let you keep tabs on the total cost of all the items you enter — so you can go through your house and "total up" what your bill should be.

PLANNING THE ROUTE

First, calculate the cost per kilowatt-hour by dividing your total electric bill by the number of kilowatt-hours used and storing the result in memory 0. Next, set up a loop (label 0) that takes watts entered, multiplies by hours used per day, converts to kilowatt-hours per month (30.4 days per month), and multiplies by cost per kilowatt-hour (stored in memory 0) to get the cost to run the appliance for a month. This cost is then summed to memory 1 for a running total. You then loop back for the wattage entry of another appliance to get its cost per month. (When you're finished, RCL 1 will give you total monthly cost for all items tested.)

MAKING TRACKS

Key in the program from the *Making Tracks* chart on the next page.

MAKING TRACKS

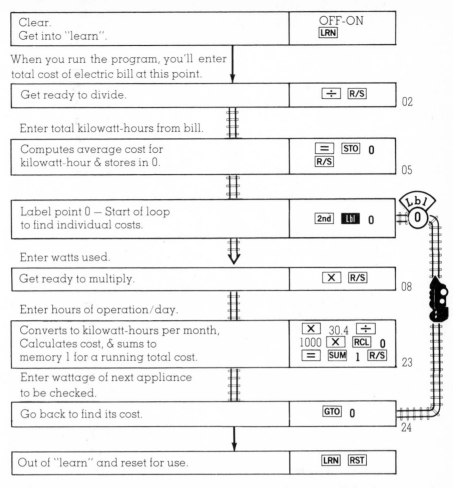

Clear. Get into "learn".	OFF-ON LRN
When you run the program, you'll enter total cost of electric bill at this point.	
Get ready to divide.	÷ R/S 02
Enter total kilowatt-hours from bill.	
Computes average cost for kilowatt-hour & stores in 0.	= STO 0 R/S 05
Label point 0 — Start of loop to find individual costs.	2nd Lbl 0
Enter watts used.	
Get ready to multiply.	X R/S 08
Enter hours of operation/day.	
Converts to kilowatt-hours per month, Calculates cost, & sums to memory 1 for a running total cost.	X 30.4 ÷ 1000 X RCL 0 = SUM 1 R/S 23
Enter wattage of next appliance to be checked.	
Go back to find its cost.	GTO 0 24
Out of "learn" and reset for use.	LRN RST

RUNNING IT

Let's say that your electric bill for last month was $42.47 for 1000 kilowatt-hours. What's the cost per month of using a 100-watt light for 12 hours/day and a toaster that draws 5 amps of current used 15 minutes/day (0.25 hours)?

PRESS	DISPLAY/COMMENTS	
2nd FIX 2	**0.00**	Rounds to nearest cent.
42.57 R/S	**42.57**	Electric bill entry.
1000 R/S	**0.04**	About 4¢/kWh average cost.
100 R/S	**100.00**	Light bulb wattage.
12 R/S	**1.55**	Cost $1.55 for 100 watt bulb.
5 X 115 = R/S	**575.00**	Wattage of toaster.
.25 R/S	**0.19**	19¢ per month for toaster.
RCL 1	**1.74**	Total cost for both items.

Note: If a new group of items (and new running total) is to be tested, use an INV 2nd C.t key sequence to clear memories, press RST , and begin.

CAR FEVER: EVALUATING PAYMENT ALTERNATIVES

In this example, consider a situation where you've found a car you'd like to buy, and need a $3400 loan. Checking at a local bank, you find that they'll gladly give you a 42-month loan at a 0.9% per month interest charge. In making your decisions on the car and the loan, it would be handy to have a program that would let you know exactly *what your monthly payments* will be for different payment plans (payoff in 1 year, 2 years, 5 months, etc.). With your calculator helping out, it's easy to create a program that will let you tabulate the number of payments in a plan (n), the payment amount, and the total amount you'd pay for the loan (the total interest charge).

DESTINATION

You'd like to set up a program that lets you enter the total loan amount, press R/S ; enter the monthly interest rate, press R/S again, — and then have your calculator calculate and display in order:
- (n) — The number of payment months — in successive 1 month steps (n = 1, 2, 3, ...).
- (PMT) — The payment amount for a loan with n number of payments.
- The total interest charge if the loan was paid off in n payments.

You'd like the program to continue to display these alternatives until you stop things with the R/S key.

PLANNING THE ROUTE

First, store the loan amount in memory 0 and the interest rate in memory 1. Then label and create a loop to evaluate the payment formula:

$\text{PMT} = \text{Loan amt} \times \dfrac{i}{(1 - (1 + i)^{-n})}$. The first step will be to generate

successive values of n (using a counting sequence such as 1 SUM **2**, RCL **2**, works well for this.) Then display n with a pause, and continue on to calculate and display the payment amount needed for a loan with n payments. After pausing to display this, multiply the payment amount by n, and subtract the loan amount to calculate your total interest charge. Display this with a pause, then loop back to the beginning and continue.

MAKING TRACKS

Follow the program logic, and carefully enter the program steps from the flow chart on the following page.

MAKING TRACKS

| Clear calculator and get into "learn". | OFF-ON
 `LRN` | |

At this point, you'll enter loan amount.

| Stores loan amount. | `STO` 0 `R/S` | 02 |

Enter interest rate.

| Stores interest. | `STO` 1 | |

| Labels start of loop. | `2nd` `Lbl` 0 | 04 |

| Adds 1 to n each loop and displays it. | `CLR` 1 `SUM` 2 `RCL` 2
 `2nd` `Pause` `2nd` `Pause` | 10 |

| Calculates & displays PMT amount. | `RCL` 0 `X`
 `RCL` 1 `÷` `(` 1
 `−` `(` 1 `+`
 `RCL` 1 `)` `yˣ`
 `RCL` 2 `+/−` `)`
 `=` `2nd` `Pause`
 `2nd` `Pause` | 29 |

| Calculate & display *interest* amount. | `X` `RCL` 2 `=`
 `−` `RCL` 0 `=`
 `2nd` `Pause` `2nd` `Pause` | 37 |

| Return & do it again. | `GTO` 0 | 38 |

| Out of "learn", reset, fix decimal at 2 places. | `LRN` `RST`
 `2nd` `FIX` 2 | |

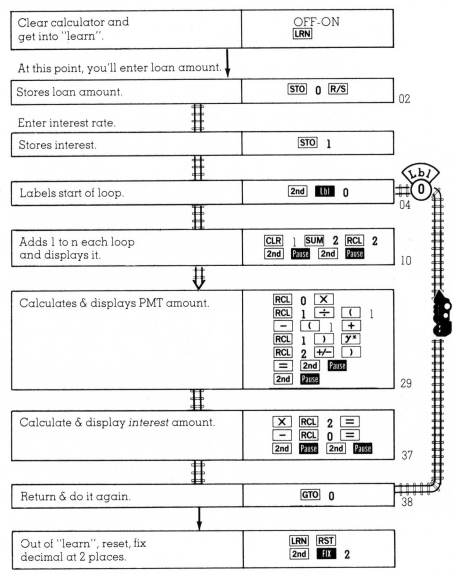

RUNNING IT

To check the alternatives on a $3400 loan, with 0.9% monthly interest:

PRESS	DISPLAY/COMMENTS
3400 R/S	**3400.00** Enter monthly payment
0.009 R/S	Enter decimal interest rate and calculator then displays
	1.00 n = 1.
	3430.60 Payment amount.
	30.60 Total interest charge for n = 1.
	2.00 n (2 payments).
	1722.98 Payment amount.
	45.97 Total interest charge for n = 2.
	⋮

To stop program press R/S whenever you wish. To check one particular payment alternative (say n = 42 months), just store n − 1 (41) in memory 2, and press GTO 0 R/S (or SBR 0).

41 STO 2	**41.00**
GTO 0 R/S	**42.00**
	97.57 per month on 42-month loan.
	698.09 Total interest for 42-month loan.
	⋮

INTERESTING POINTS ON INTEREST

As you've seen in this chapter, interest rates are an important part of any business or financial calculation. The *terminology* used in describing interest rates can be a little baffling, though. It's important to be certain that you understand the interest rates involved when calculating for any business decision. Be sure the interest rate in any calculation is for the *same length of time as your payment (or investment) period.* If you're doing a calculation involving monthly payments, the interest rate must be expressed as a *monthly* rate.

Now, let's say that you're given an *effective yearly* rate, and need to get to an equivalent monthly compound interest rate. You can calculate equivalent interest rates for different intervals by using the compound interest formula. For example, suppose you deposit amount (A) for a year at 15% per year interest.

(You would have A × (1 + .15) at the end of the year.) Now say you would like to know what monthly compounded interest rate (i) is equivalent to 15% yearly compounded interest. To determine the equivalent monthly compounded rate, assume you deposit the same amount (A) in an account which pays i per month.

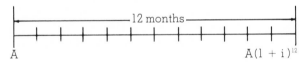

The interest rates will be equivalent if the final amounts are equal, after the *same time period.*
$A (1 + .15) = A (1 + i)^{12}$
Now the equation may be solved for i.
Dividing both sides by A gives:
$(1 + .15) = (1 + i)^{12}$
taking the 12th root, $^{12}\sqrt{(1 + .15)} = (1 + i)$
subtracting 1 from both sides,
$^{12}\sqrt{(1 + .15)} - 1 = i$
On your calculator [( ] 1 [+] .15 [ )] [INV] [yˣ] 12 [−] 1 [=] .0117149 or about 1.17% monthly interest.

This gives you a basic guide to find equivalent interest rates for different time periods. However, in all cases involving interest, if you're in doubt as to how it's actually figured, check with the bank or lending institution you're considering to see exactly how *they* figure their interest.

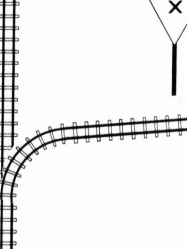

AN INTRODUCTION

Mathematics is all around us — the language of numbers allows us to live our everyday lives more easily, handle the work we do, as well as learn about and describe the world we live in. Up to this point, you've learned about programming and the basic building blocks of programs — and seen some applications of programming in financial situations. In this chapter we'll explore some specific areas in math that are particularly suited to your programmable calculator. Again, with your calculator handling *tedious repetitive* computations — you'll find yourself free to focus on the hows and whys of mathematical relationships and techniques. The areas we'll cover in this chapter include:

- **Polar Plots:** Your calculator makes all sorts of accurate graphing possible with speed and ease. In this section we'll investigate polar plots — the "butterfly and flower" diagrams you may have investigated in your classwork.

- **Evaluating Integrals:** This program finds the value of the integral of functions (area "under the curve") using Simpson's approximation.

- **Triangle Tracking:** There's a formula that enables you to calculate the area of a triangle, knowing only the length of the sides. This program handles it easily.

- **The Limit:** Programming simple iterative loops allows you to easily watch functions converge to a limit, or diverge towards infinity (∞). This section illustrates a general technique for setting up these programs, and investigates the function:

$$\frac{\ln x}{x - 1} \text{ , as x approaches 1.}$$

- **Linear Regression/Trend Line Analysis:** These rather formidable sounding terms refer to techniques that address one of the oldest problems in the world: can you predict the future, based on past events? We will discuss a program that allows you to predict trends and "interpolate" from your known data points.

Programming allows you an added dimension in exploring mathematics — the dimension of "discovery by watching in action". You can program a function into your calculator, and easily see it evaluated for a variety of input variable values. In this way, you can see things working quickly — in a way that can often be obscured by tedious computation.

POLAR PLOTS

You've already seen your calculator in action handling simple straight line calculations or more complex iterative loops. One application it especially "shines at", however, is in helping you to easily and accurately graph the behavior of functions. Normally, graphing even a simple function is a tedious process. You evaluate the function for one set of values for its variables, plot one point, change the value of the variables in some specified way, evaluate the function all over again, plot another point — and so on. Even with a powerful, standard non-programmable calculator — it's a time-consuming and error prone process.

Your programmable calculator was made-to-order for graphing. It loves handling repetitive calculation, and it can automatically step the variables for you so you get your points to plot just as fast as you can write them down!

DESTINATION

In this case we'll consider polar plots. Here, one of the variables in the function we'll consider is an angle whose value will run from 0 to 360°; and our plot will be made on polar coordinate axes. Let's say we want to graph the function:

$$r = a \sin n\theta,$$
where $a = 5$ and
$$n = 2, \text{ for values of } \theta \text{ from } 0° \text{ to } 360°.$$

To plot any point on this graph we'll need a value for the radius r (distance from the origin to our point); and θ, the angle counterclockwise from the x axis.

Point A shown is (4, 30°), where $r = 4$, and $\theta = 30°$. If the value for r is *negative*, r is simply plotted in the *opposite* direction. Point B shown is (− 4, 30°). (The value of r is still 4, except in this case we plot it along the 30° line in the *opposite* direction.)

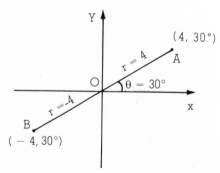

To plot a polar graph of r = 5 sin 2θ, we'll start with θ equal 0°, evaluate r, increase θ in 10 degree steps and display an r value for each so that we can create a table of r and θ values easily. the program will allow you to change the values of a and n easily so that other functions of this type can be plotted. To run the program you:

- Enter the value of a, press R/S .
- Enter n, press R/S again.
- The calculator will then start θ at 0°, pause (displaying it), then calculate r and halt with the value in the display.
- Pressing R/S again will increment θ by 10°, display it, calculate a new value for r and halt with r in the display. Continuing to press R/S will allow you to tabulate all the values for θ and r needed to complete the polar plot.

PLANNING THE ROUTE

To begin, we'll store the "a" value in memory 0 and the r value in memory 1. We'll be using memory 2 to store Θ. Then to evaluate the function, begin with a label, recall memory 2 and pause to display Θ; then solve for r = a sin nΘ and halt to show the "r" value. Then sum 10 to memory 2 (to add 10° to Θ), loop back and repeat for the new value of Θ.

MAKING TRACKS

Key in the program carefully from the flow chart on the following page.

MAKING TRACKS

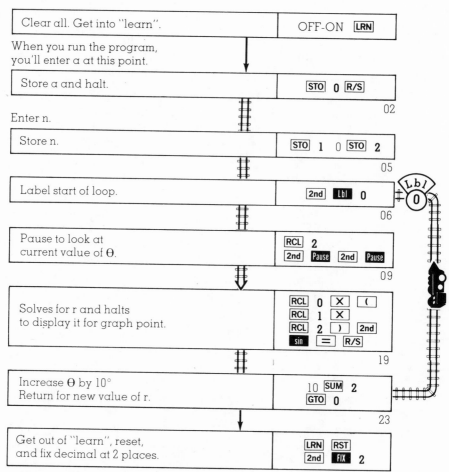

Clear all. Get into "learn".	OFF-ON [LRN]

When you run the program,
you'll enter a at this point.

Store a and halt.	[STO] 0 [R/S]

02

Enter n.

Store n.	[STO] 1 0 [STO] 2

05

Label start of loop.	[2nd] [Lbl] 0

06

Pause to look at current value of θ.	[RCL] 2 [2nd] [Pause] [2nd] [Pause]

09

Solves for r and halts to display it for graph point.	[RCL] 0 [X] [( ] [RCL] 1 [X] [RCL] 2 [ )] [2nd] [sin] [=] [R/S]

19

Increase θ by 10° Return for new value of r.	10 [SUM] 2 [GTO] 0

23

Get out of "learn", reset, and fix decimal at 2 places.	[LRN] [RST] [2nd] [FIX] 2

RUNNING IT

To plot r = 5 sin 2 θ, after your program is keyed in:

PRESS	**DISPLAY/COMMENTS**	
[INV] [2nd] [C.t] [RST]	**0**	Clear machine and reset.
5 [R/S]	**5.00**	Enter a = 5
2 [R/S]		Enter n = 2
	0.00	First θ value: θ = 0°
	0.00	First r value: r = 0
[R/S]	**10.00**	θ = 10°
	1.71	r = 1.71
[R/S]	**20.00**	θ = 20°
	3.21	r = 3.21

As you continue to push [R/S] , you'll generate a table of values for θ and r:

θ	r
30.00	4.33
40.00	4.92
.	.
.	.
.	.
360	0.00

The graph of the function will appear as follows when plotted on polar coordinate paper. (*Note:* remember for negative values of r, your plot will go in the opposite direction. As you plot, you'll draw the "lobe" in Quadrant I, then Quadrant IV, then Quadrant III, and finally, Quadrant II.)

Graph of r = 5 sin 2θ

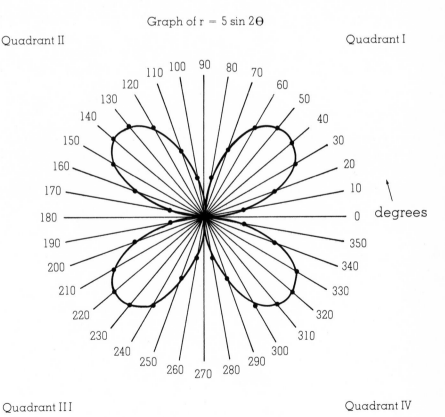

EVALUATING INTEGRALS: SIMPSON'S RULE

If you've had any calculus courses, you're probably familiar with the integral symbol "$\int$". This symbol stands for "the integral of", and $_a\!\int^b f(x)dx$ is read "the integral of f(x) from a to b" — and represents the *area* under the curve y = f(x) from point a to point b as shown in the figure.

If you know the techniques of integral calculus, you know that there are methods allowing you to evaluate most integrals exactly. You also know that in some cases this evaluation may be extremely difficult, or even impossible! In these cases, approximation techniques are sometimes used. One of these approximation methods is called *Simpson's approximation*.

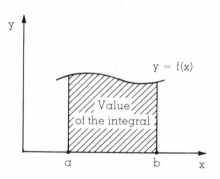

When using Simpson's approximation (or Simpson's rule, as it's often called), you divide the area under the curve into an *even* number of parts (n). The width of each part, w, is then given by: $w = \frac{b-a}{n}$. In the figure shown, we've divided the area into 6 parts, so $w = \frac{b-a}{6}$. To compute the approximate total area under the curve (the approximate value of the integral), you use the following formula:

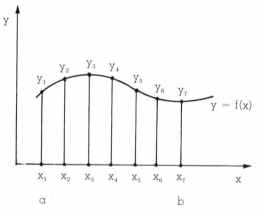

$$\text{Area} = \frac{w}{3} \times (Y_1 + 4Y_2 + 2Y_3 + 4Y_4 + \ldots + 2Y_{n-1} + 4Y_n + Y_{n+1}).$$

This formidable looking formula is actually quite easy to evaluate with the program we'll develop in this section.

Here Y_1 = the Y value with x = a
$\quad Y_2$ = the Y value with x = a + w
$\quad Y_3$ = the Y value with x = a + w + w,
$$\vdots$$
$\qquad$ etc.
$$\vdots$$
$\quad Y_{n+1}$ = the Y value with x = b

As an example, we'll write a program for (and evaluate) the integral of $y = 2x^2 + 3x - 1$ from $a = 1$ to $b = 5$, using $n = 6$. (Note, the integral approximation gets more accurate as n is made larger.)

DESTINATION

We'll construct a program with a subroutine that repeatedly solves the equation $y = 2x^2 + 3x - 1$, for each value of x between a and b. Then using these values Simpson's approximation will be computed. The program will be constructed so that you'll:

- Enter n (number of divisions — must be an *even* integer). and press STO **0**.
- Enter b and press STO **1**.
- Enter a and press STO **2**.
- Press RST R/S , and after a wait, the display will read the integral of the function. To evaluate the integral of any new function all that must be altered will be subroutine 1, which evaluates the function. Just press GTO **1** while out of LEARN mode, press LRN , enter the new function (remembering that x is in memory 2) and end with an INV SBR . Press LRN again, enter your new values for a, b, and n and continue.

PLANNING THE ROUTE

Since $y = f(x) = 2x^2 + 3x - 1$ needs to be evaluated many times in this program, and needs to be easily changeable so that other integrals can be evaluated, we'll place it in a subroutine at the end of the program. We'll begin the program by calculating $w = \frac{b-a}{n}$, storing it and recalling as we need it. We'll include program steps to find the right multiplying number (called coefficients) for each "Y" term in the Simpson's rule formula:

$$\text{Area} = \frac{w}{3}(Y_1 + 4Y_2 + 2Y_3 + 4Y_4 + \ldots + 2Y_{n-1} + 4Y_n + Y_{n+1}).$$

(Note that the coefficients of Y will either be 1, 2, or 4 depending on which term we're evaluating.) We'll use subroutine 1 to evaluate each Y term, multiply by the correct coefficient and sum the result to memory 3. Then we'll step to the next x value, determine a new coefficient, a new Y value, and repeat for n steps. At the end of these steps, we'll compute Y_{n+1}, sum it to 3, multiply by $\frac{w}{3}$ and display the final result.

MAKING TRACKS

Enter the program carefully from the flow diagram on the following page.

RUNNING IT

Again, keep in mind that this program evaluates the integral of $y = 2x^2 + 3x - 1$. To change to another function:
- Be sure you're out of "learn".
- Press GTO 1.
- Press LRN
- Enter the new function.
- End with an INV SBR sequence.

To evaluate $2x^2 + 3x - 1$ for $a = 1$, $b = 5$, $n = 6$:

PRESS	DISPLAY/COMMENTS
6 STO 0	**6.** Enter n,
5 STO 1	**5.** Enter b,
1 STO 2	**1.** Enter a,
RST R/S	**114.66667** The approximate integral value — give your calculator some time to finish.

MAKING TRACKS

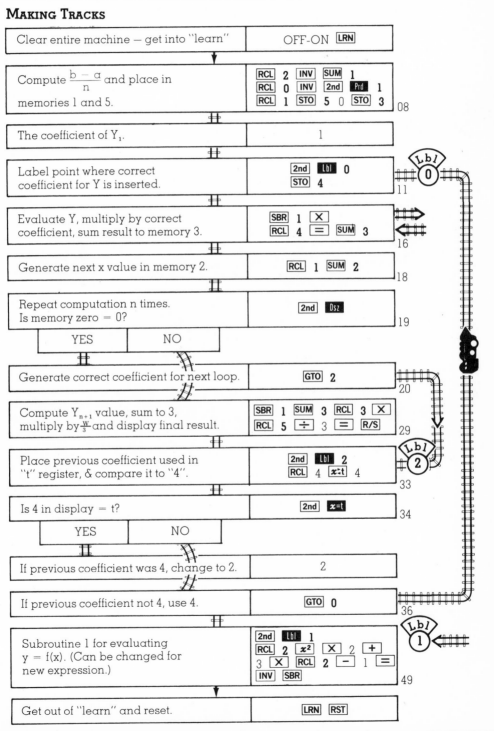

Clear entire machine — get into "learn"	OFF-ON [LRN]
Compute $\dfrac{b-a}{n}$ and place in memories 1 and 5.	RCL 2 INV SUM 1 RCL 0 INV 2nd Prd 1 RCL 1 STO 5 0 STO 3 *08*
The coefficient of Y_1.	1
Label point where correct coefficient for Y is inserted.	2nd Lbl 0 STO 4 *11*
Evaluate Y, multiply by correct coefficient, sum result to memory 3.	SBR 1 × RCL 4 = SUM 3 *16*
Generate next x value in memory 2.	RCL 1 SUM 2 *18*
Repeat computation n times. Is memory zero = 0?	2nd Dsz *19*
YES — NO	
Generate correct coefficient for next loop.	GTO 2 *20*
Compute Y_{n+1} value, sum to 3, multiply by $\frac{w}{3}$ and display final result.	SBR 1 SUM 3 RCL 3 × RCL 5 ÷ 3 = R/S *29*
Place previous coefficient used in "t" register, & compare it to "4".	2nd Lbl 2 RCL 4 x⇄t 4 *33*
Is 4 in display = t?	2nd x=t *34*
YES — NO	
If previous coefficient was 4, change to 2.	2
If previous coefficient not 4, use 4.	GTO 0 *36*
Subroutine 1 for evaluating y = f(x). (Can be changed for new expression.)	2nd Lbl 1 RCL 2 x² × 2 + 3 × RCL 2 − 1 = INV SBR *49*
Get out of "learn" and reset.	LRN RST

TRIANGLE TRACKING

When working with triangles, most of us remember one formula for computing the area: $A = \frac{1}{2}bh$ (where b is the length of the base, and h is the height). There are cases, however, where the height may be difficult to compute, or you don't know any of the angles in the triangle, — all you know are the length of its 3 sides a, b, and c. In this case you can compute the triangle's area with a formula known as *Heron's formula.*

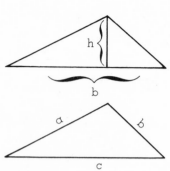

This technique is especially handy to use where you're computing land areas on an odd-shaped piece of land. Most odd-shaped land parcels can easily be divided, using a survey map, into rectangles and triangular shaped areas. The areas of the rectangles are easy to compute, but the triangle areas can be tricky — because in some cases all you know is the length of the triangle's sides. This program handles Heron's formula easily.

Odd-Shaped
Land Parcel

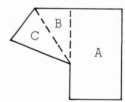

Odd-Shaped
Parcel Divided Up

DESTINATION

Heron's formula states that the area of any triangle equals $\sqrt{S(S - a)\,(S - b)\,(S - c)}$ where a, b, and c are the lengths of the three sides and $S = \frac{1}{2}(a + b + c)$. You'll want a program that allows you to:

- Enter a and press R/S .
- Enter b and press R/S .
- Enter c and press R/S .

The calculator will then calculate and display the area of the triangle.

PLANNING THE ROUTE

First, provide for storing a in memory 1, b in memory 2, and c in memory 3. Then calculate the value of S, where $S = \frac{1}{2}(a + b + c)$, and store this in memory 4. Then calculate the area $= \sqrt{S(S - a)\,(S - b)\,(S - c)}$ by recalling the memories as needed. Include an RST at the end to reset for the next triangle calculation.

MAKING TRACKS

Key in the program from the *Making Tracks* flow chart below.

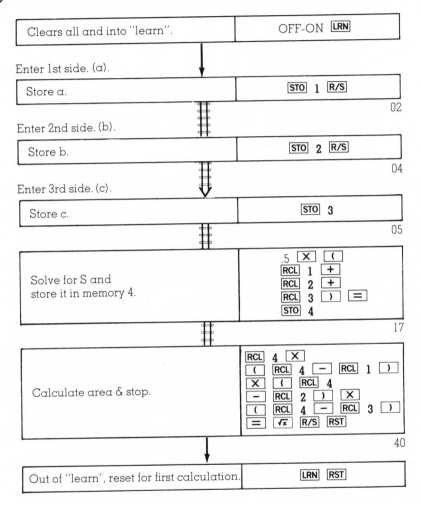

Clears all and into "learn".	OFF-ON [LRN]

Enter 1st side. (a).

Store a.	[STO] 1 [R/S] 02

Enter 2nd side. (b).

Store b.	[STO] 2 [R/S] 04

Enter 3rd side. (c).

Store c.	[STO] 3 05

Solve for S and store it in memory 4.	.5 [X] [(] [RCL] 1 [+] [RCL] 2 [+] [RCL] 3 [)] [=] [STO] 4 17

Calculate area & stop.	[RCL] 4 [X] [(] [RCL] 4 [−] [RCL] 1 [)] [X] [(] [RCL] 4 [−] [RCL] 2 [)] [X] [(] [RCL] 4 [−] [RCL] 3 [)] [=] [√x] [R/S] [RST] 40

Out of "learn", reset for first calculation.	[LRN] [RST]

RUNNING IT

As an example, find the area of this triangle:

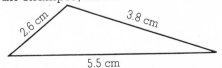

2.6 cm   3.8 cm

5.5 cm

Note: It doesn't matter which side is
a, b, or c as long as all 3 are used.

PRESS	DISPLAY/COMMENTS	
2.6 [R/S]	**2.6**	Enter side a.
3.8 [R/S]	**3.8**	Enter side b.
5.5 [R/S]	**4.3914341**	The area for this triangle is 4.39 cm².

THE LIMIT

Your calculator can add a new dimension to one of the more interesting explorations in mathematics — investigating limits of functions. In these situations you examine the behavior of some function ($f(x)$), as its variable (x) approaches some specific value. The function in some cases may "go to infinity" or "*diverge*" right at the limit point, or it may converge to a specific limit value.

At any rate, your calculator, by making rapid repetitive calculations possible, allows you to examine the behavior of functions near limits, and determine what functional limits will be — even in some not so obvious situations. For example, what is the limit of the function $f(x) = \dfrac{\ln x}{x-1}$, as x approaches 1?

(This is written $\displaystyle\lim_{x \to 1} \dfrac{\ln x}{x-1}$.) Notice that at $x = 1$, both ln x and x–1 have the value 0, and $\dfrac{0}{0}$ is an "undefined" quantity. With your calculator, though, we can set up a program that will let you "watch the limit happen".

DESTINATION

We'll work up a program that lets you store the limit point (in this case 1) in memory 1, and store some number you'll be coming from (say 4) in memory 2. When you press R/S the calculator will evaluate the function $\dfrac{\ln x}{x-1}$ for values of x that move from 4 to 1 (halving the distance to one each time). The value of x will be displayed (for 2 pauses), followed by the value of the function (for 4 pauses).

PLANNING THE ROUTE

In our program we'll generate a series of x values that approach (but never reach 1) by halving the difference between the current x value and one, then adding that number to 1. We'll pause to display the current x value, then use a subroutine to compute and display f(x). We'll then loop to the beginning and repeat.

Making Tracks

Enter the program carefully from the flow chart provided.

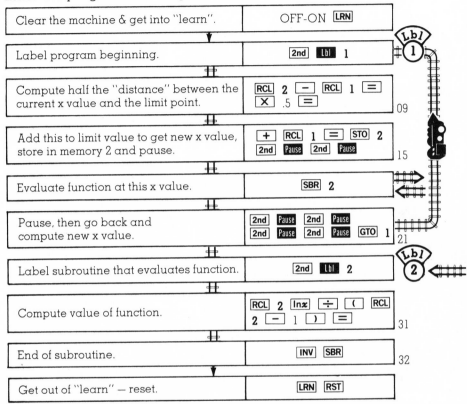

Clear the machine & get into "learn".	OFF-ON [LRN]	
Label program beginning.	[2nd] [Lbl] 1	
Compute half the "distance" between the current x value and the limit point.	[RCL] 2 [−] [RCL] 1 [=] [×] .5 [=]	09
Add this to limit value to get new x value, store in memory 2 and pause.	[+] [RCL] 1 [=] [STO] 2 [2nd] [Pause] [2nd] [Pause]	15
Evaluate function at this x value.	[SBR] 2	
Pause, then go back and compute new x value.	[2nd] [Pause] [2nd] [Pause] [2nd] [Pause] [2nd] [Pause] [GTO] 1	21
Label subroutine that evaluates function.	[2nd] [Lbl] 2	
Compute value of function.	[RCL] 2 [lnx] [÷] [(] [RCL] 2 [−] 1 [)] [=]	31
End of subroutine.	[INV] [SBR]	32
Get out of "learn" — reset.	[LRN] [RST]	

Running It

To watch this function approach its limit at $x = 1$, just enter the limit point and a starting value for x as shown below.

Press	Display/Comments
1 [STO] 1	**1.** Store limit point.
4 [STO] 2	**4.** Store point you wish to approach from.
[RST] [R/S]	**2.5** x value
	0.6108605 f(x)
	1.75 x value
	0.7461544 f(x)
	1.375
	0.84921 etc.

As you watch the display, it will become obvious for this function that as x approaches 1, the limit of f(x) approaches 1.

LINEAR REGRESSION

As most of us progress through school or business, there will be times when we would like to predict the outcome of some future event — based on our knowledge of how similar things have gone in the past. You might want to predict the effects of changes in diet on animal growth in the biology lab. Or if you're a businessman, you might want to predict what effect an increase in advertising will have on product sales. In either case you want to be able to take a known set of data, and use it to establish a straight line graph, and then predict from the line what the outcome should be in the future.

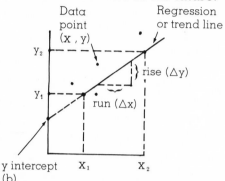

Data point (x, y)

Regression or trend line

rise (△y)

run (△x)

y intercept (b)

x_1

x_2

y_2

y_1

The way you normally do this is to "draw" a linear (straight) line that best represents the graph of all of your known data or test points. Then you can extend the line either way to predict similar events. Data points are usually expressed as two numbers, an x coordinate and a y coordinate for each point you're plotting.

Determining and drawing the *best* straight line through a variety of data points is pretty much a hit or miss matter when drawing a graph. With your calculator, however, you can take this program and handle several aspects of the problem easily.

First of all, any straight line graph can be expressed as the equation: y = mx + b. Here m is the *slope* of the line, and b is called the "y intercept". The slope (m) of the line, is the ratio of its "rise" to its "run" and the intercept (b) is where the line crosses the y axis. Once you know the slope and intercept of a line you can easily draw it. Then, with your graph you can extend the line to use it in making calculations and predictions with your data — as we'll show.

With your calculator, you can calculate the slope and intercept of a line through your data points. Finding these values can be rather involved, however, and this is an area where programmability will bring a real payoff. The formula for calculating the slope is given by:

$$m = \frac{\frac{\sum_{i=1}^{n} x_i y_i}{n} - \bar{x}\bar{y}}{\sigma x^2}$$

The formula for the intercept is:

$$b = \bar{y} - m\bar{x}$$

$\displaystyle\sum_{i=1}^{n} x_i y_i$ means the sum of all data coordinates multiplied together, starting at 1 and going to n; $(x_1 y_1, x_2 y_2, ...)$. With the help of some special keys on your calculator and the program we'll develop, you'll be able to solve for m and b with a fraction of the effort normally involved in handling these complex formulas.

The program will also allow you to use your data to make predictions. Once you find m and b, you'll be able to enter a new "x" value and get its corresponding "predicted" "y" value on the line using the formula $y = mx + b$. Or you can enter a "y" value and "predict" the corresponding "x" value on the line using the equation $x = \dfrac{y - b}{m}$.

This program also lets you find a number called the coefficient of determination (labeled r^2). The number r (computed from r^2 with a simple $\boxed{\sqrt{x}}$ keystroke) is called the absolute value of the correlation coefficient. This is a measure of how well your data points correspond or correlate to your line. This helps determine the accuracy of predictions you make from your line. A value close to 1 indicates a high correlation. (The calculator could fit your points accurately to a trend line.) A value close to zero indicates that the sets of data have a low correlation and the trend line developed by the calculator is not as reliable for predictions. The formula for r^2 is:

$$r^2 = \frac{m^2 \, \sigma x^2}{\sigma y^2}.$$

The program we're about to embark on involves many, many calculations and will pretty well "load up" your calculator. The important point is that with your calculator handling the difficult mathematics, you can use the powerful tools of linear regression for prediction and planning, without getting stopped by the mass of computation involved.

DESTINATION

We'll develop a program that allows you to enter all of your data points easily, and then compute m, b, and r^2. Then you'll want to be able to compute a "y" value for any given "x" value, or for any given y to find a corresponding "x" value. To do all of this you'll follow these steps:

- Enter data points by entering x, pressing x≈t , then entering y and pressing R/S . You'll do this until all of your (x, y) data points are entered.
- Then to find m, press SBR **0**.
- To find b, press SBR **1**.
- To find r^2, press SBR **2**. Then √x to find r .
  (Remember a "r" value near one means good correlation, a value near zero means that the calculator could not reliably correlate your data to a straight line.)
- To predict what value on the line that y will have for a given "x" value, just enter the "x" value and press SBR **3**.
- To predict what value on the line that x will have for a particular y, enter the "y" value and press SBR **4**.

PLANNING THE ROUTE

The first step will be to enter all the data points using the special data collection keys on your calculator. These are the 2nd Σ+ , 2nd x̄ , and 2nd σ2 keys on the lower right of the machine, described at the end of *Chapter 2*.

Rather than pushing 2nd Σ+ for each entry, we'll include a simple sequence in the program to help in entering data points. Then we'll divide the rest of the program into five subroutines to calculate m, b, r^2, and to find x or y. Follow the flow chart carefully as steps have been conserved using memory arithmetic.

MAKING TRACKS

Key in the flow chart carefully from the *Making Tracks* chart on the next page.

MAKING TRACKS

Clears all and into "learn".	OFF-ON [LRN]

(You'll enter x press [x:t] , then y & [R/S])

Enters each data point & resets.	[2nd] [Σ+] [R/S] [RST]	03
Identifies subroutine 0.	[2nd] [Lbl] 0	Lbl 0
Solve for the slope, m.	[RCL] 5 [÷] [RCL] 0 [−] [2nd] [x̄] [X] [INV] [2nd] [x̄] [=] [÷] [INV] [2nd] [σ²] [=] [INV] [SBR]	16
Identifies subroutine 1.	[2nd] [Lbl] 1	Lbl 1
Calculates the y intercept, b.	[SBR] 0 [X] [INV] [2nd] [x̄] [+/−] [+] [2nd] [x̄] [=] [INV] [SBR]	25
Identifies subroutine 2.	[2nd] [Lbl] 2	Lbl 2
Solves for r^2.	[SBR] 0 [x²] [÷] [2nd] [σ²] [X] [INV] [2nd] [σ²] [=] [INV] [SBR]	34

You'll enter an x value.

Subroutine 3.	[2nd] [Lbl] 3	Lbl 3
Finds y to correspond to entered value of x.	[STO] 7 [SBR] 0 [2nd] [Prd] 7 [SBR] 1 [SUM] 7 [RCL] 7 [INV] [SBR]	42

You'll enter a y value.

Identifies subroutine 4.	[2nd] [Lbl] 4	Lbl 4
Finds x to correspond to entered value of y.	[STO] 7 [SBR] 1 [INV] [SUM] 7 [SBR] 0 [INV] [2nd] [Prd] 7 [RCL] 7 [INV] [SBR]	

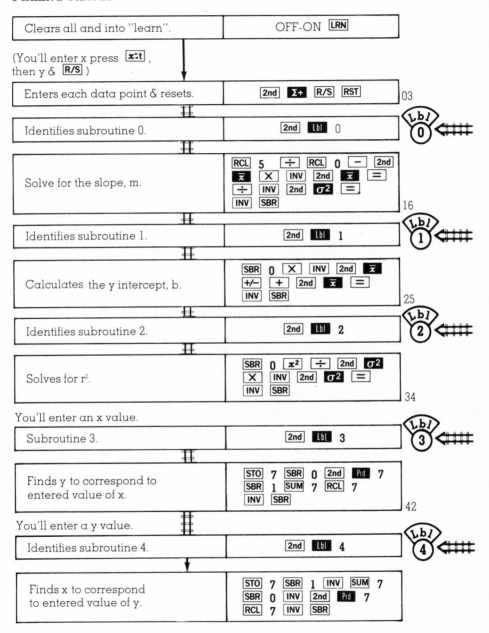

Note: You won't need to leave "learn" as all 50 steps are used and the calculator leaves "learn" automatically.

RUNNING IT

Test Scores vs. Performance: An Example

Let's say you're a businessman and your sales manager is spending a considerable sum on a test for prospective sales employees. You'd like to see if this test is actually telling you anything about how well the employee will function in the field. Does a higher test score mean superior sales performance? How strong a *correlation* is there between these two factors in your business? If there is a good correlation, you'd like to know the slope and the intercept of the straight line, so you can use these values for future predictions. Also, you'd like to know specifically what a test score of 9 predicts in sales performance; and what value test score would indicate a sales performance of 75.

Let's say you have samples of the test scores for 10 employees, along with records on sales performance expressed as the percentage of the time that each employee exceeded his or her weekly sales goals last year. The data is tabulated below:

Employee	Employee Test Score (x)	Employee Sales Performance (y)
Jerry	5	10
Ross	13	30
Joe	8	30
Ralph	10	40
Mary	15	60
Gary	20	50
Dean	4	20
Carole	16	60
Ted	18	50
Alecia	6	20

Follow the steps below in entering the data, and analyzing it to make a prediction:

PRESS	DISPLAY/COMMENTS	
INV 2nd C.t RST	Clear memories and RST to get started. Then enter your data.*	
5 x:t 10 R/S	**1.**	*Note:* your calculator
13 x:t 30 R/S	**2.**	keeps count of each
8 x:t 30 R/S	**3.**	data point you enter.
10 x:t 40 R/S	**4.**	
15 x:t 60 R/S	**5.**	
20 x:t 50 R/S	**6.**	
4 x:t 20 R/S	**7.**	
16 x:t 60 R/S	**8.**	
18 x:t 50 R/S	**9.**	
6 x:t 20 R/S	**10.**	You've entered your 10 data points. To find the slope
SBR 0	**2.6837607**	= m To find the "y" intercept
SBR 1	**6.1367521**	To find the correlation factor
SBR 2	**0.7497339**	= r^2
√x	**0.8658717**	= r There is a fairly good correlation – the r value is reasonably close to +1. What sales performance would a test score of 9 predict?
9 SBR 3	**30.290598**	Prediction: about a 30% sales performance above goal. What test score would indicate a 75% above goal sales performance record?
75 SBR 4	**25.659236**	An employee with a score of about 26 should achieve a 75% above goal sales rating.

*Note: If you make a mistake entering any data point, you can remove the bad point by re-entering it following this sequence: re-enter "x" value, press x:t . Then re-enter y value and press INV 2nd Σ+ . Then proceed with correct data points as shown above.

SCIENCE TRACKS: AN INTRODUCTION

Your programmable calculator can be an invaluable aid in your explorations in science classes, or as you find science applied around the home and in everyday life. Scientists often work with mathematical "models" of phenomena — numerical descriptions of how the world is put together. Your programmable calculator, equipped with the AOS entry system and scientific notation, is a "natural" for helping you in quickly and accurately handling scientific math. With looping programs, you can actually watch events, experiments, and natural phenomena *unfold* as time goes on. You see mathematical models or systems in action, rather than just as formulas to be evaluated.

By exploring science with your calculator, you will find that your mind is free to focus on the whys and hows of physical laws or natural events.

The formulas you'll find in the various sections of this chapter are usually labelled in a common sense way — and relate directly to a diagram or description of the problem that's given. This chapter includes a brief selection of topics taken from several areas of science, including:

- **Projectile motion:** A simple program lets you "watch" an object move through space in a "ballistic trajectory".
- **The Simple Pendulum:** You plug in the essential parameters, and "watch" it swing using this program.
- **Mass and Relativity:** Using your calculator, you can "watch" the powerful and intriguing formulas of relativity in action.
- **Exponential Growth (& Decay):** Many natural phenomena follow what's called an "exponential" behavior. You can watch these systems "develop" using this program.
- **Resonance:** All types of standing structures in nature, as well as electronic devices, exhibit what's called a "resonance" behavior. This program allows you to enter a "description" of a system, and then examine its "resonance" response.

Note: All the examples in this chapter use the metric system and data must be entered in the same units as shown in each example.

PROJECTILE MOTION

Probably all of us at one time or another have tossed or hit a *projectile* into the air (baseball, golf ball, etc.). This is motion in *two* dimensions, and (if we neglect the frictional effects of the air) it usually follows a classic parabolic curve as shown below:

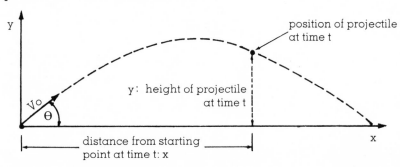

In the case of a golf ball (etc.) projected into the air with an initial speed Vo, at an angle Θ with respect to the x axis, the motion would appear as shown above. Once the ball is in the air, the only force acting on it is gravity, which accelerates it downward at $g = -9.8$ meters/second^2. The equations which describe how the distance from the starting point (x), and the height off the ground (y) vary with time as the ball flies through space are:

$$x = (Vo \cos\Theta)t$$

and $y = (Vo \sin\Theta)t + \frac{1}{2}gt^2$ (where $g = -9.8$ m/s^2).

We'll work up a program that lets us "watch" the projectile fly through space.

DESTINATION

We'll develop a program allowing us to:

- Enter a time interval for our observation, and press [STO] 1. (We can see where the ball is every ½ second, 1 second, etc.)
- Enter the intial speed Vo, and press [RST], [R/S].
- Enter the initial angle Θ in degrees, press [R/S] again.

The program will then display:

- the time of the observation in seconds, pause, then,
- the distance from the starting point (x) in meters, pause and then
- the height from the ground (y) in meters. It then will step the time by the value stored in memory 1 and continue.

PLANNING THE ROUTE

We'll begin by storing Vo and Θ, and then create a loop that first steps t to a new value, then executes a subroutine that computes x and displays it, and then computes y and displays it.

MAKING TRACKS

Carefully key in the program from the flow chart provided below:

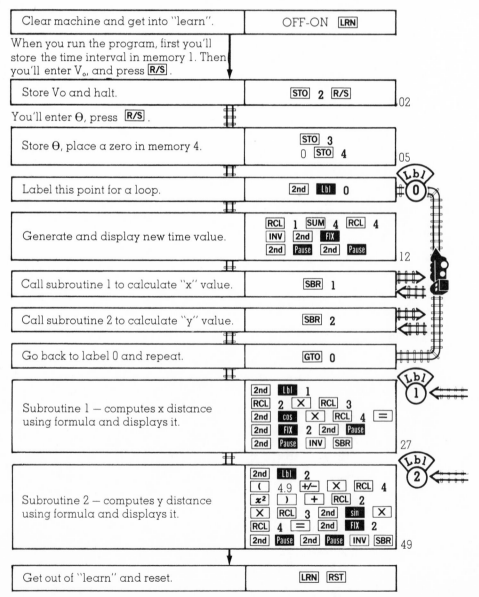

Clear machine and get into "learn".	OFF-ON [LRN]

When you run the program, first you'll store the time interval in memory 1. Then you'll enter V_o, and press [R/S].

Store Vo and halt.	[STO] 2 [R/S]

02

You'll enter Θ, press [R/S].

Store Θ, place a zero in memory 4.	[STO] 3 0 [STO] 4

05

Label this point for a loop.	[2nd] [Lbl] 0

Generate and display new time value.	[RCL] 1 [SUM] 4 [RCL] 4 [INV] [2nd] [FIX] [2nd] [Pause] [2nd] [Pause]

12

Call subroutine 1 to calculate "x" value.	[SBR] 1

Call subroutine 2 to calculate "y" value.	[SBR] 2

Go back to label 0 and repeat.	[GTO] 0

Subroutine 1 — computes x distance using formula and displays it.	[2nd] [Lbl] 1 [RCL] 2 [×] [RCL] 3 [2nd] [cos] [×] [RCL] 4 [=] [2nd] [FIX] 2 [2nd] [Pause] [2nd] [Pause] [INV] [SBR]

27

Subroutine 2 — computes y distance using formula and displays it.	[2nd] [Lbl] 2 [(] 4.9 [+/−] [×] [RCL] 4 [x^2] [)] [+] [RCL] 2 [×] [RCL] 3 [2nd] [sin] [×] [RCL] 4 [=] [2nd] [FIX] 2 [2nd] [Pause] [2nd] [Pause] [INV] [SBR]

49

Get out of "learn" and reset.	[LRN] [RST]

RUNNING IT

Let's examine the path of a bullet, fired at 130 meters per second initial speed at an angle Θ of 25° from the horizontal. We'll see where the bullet is every 0.5 seconds.

Note: The calculator must be in "degree" mode. (It's there automatically when you turn it on.)

PRESS	DISPLAY/COMMENTS
0.5 STO 1	**0.5** Store the time interval
130 RST R/S	**130.**
25	**25**
R/S	From then on in — the following numbers are displayed as the program loops — first t, then x, then y.

t	*x*	*y*
0.5	58.91	26.25
1.	117.82	50.04
1.5	176.73	71.39
2.	235.64	90.28
•	•	•
•	•	•
11	1296.02	11.44
11.5	1354.93	− 16.21

Note: When the y distance becomes *negative*, the particle has hit the ground. Remember that you can stop the program at any time, and "freeze" any readout, by simply pressing and holding R/S for a moment.

THE SIMPLE PENDULUM

The pendulum, a simple mass hanging by a light sturdy cord, is one of the oldest and most accurate timing devices used by man. Galileo is said to have observed the periodic swinging of a candleholder during a church service, and to later adopt the principle in timing his experiments on gravity and free fall.

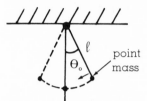

In mathematically describing the motion of a pendulum, we'll assume we have a point mass hanging from a light cord of length ℓ. The mass is pulled aside an angle Θ_0 (less than 15°) from the vertical. When released, the pendulum (if we assume no frictional losses) will swing back and forth at a steady rate — the time for one complete cycle being given by $T = 2\pi\sqrt{\frac{\ell}{g}}$,

length of the cord, and g is the acceleration due to gravity (= 9.8 m/s²). The motion is described by the equation:

$$\Theta = \Theta_0 \sin\left(\left(\frac{t}{T} \times 360\right) + 90\right).$$

DESTINATION

We'll work up a program that lets you:

- Enter the initial angle Θ_0 (the angle in degrees that the mass is pulled from vertical) press R/S .
- Enter the length of the pendulum "ℓ", press R/S .
  At this point the *period* (time for one complete oscillation) will be displayed.
- To be able to watch the pendulum as it goes through the cycle, you then enter a time interval (less than one oscillation period) at which you want to observe the motion, press R/S again — and the calculator will display:
  first, the time (with 0 being the release time) and
  then the angle of the pendulum at that time point.

The calculator will then loop and continue by incrementing the time and showing the new angle, to let you watch the pendulum swing.

PLANNING THE ROUTE

We'll begin by storing the original deflection angle (Θ_0) and the length (ℓ in *meters*). The period $T = 2\pi\sqrt{\frac{\ell}{g}}$ will be computed. The calculator will then step the current time (t) by the time interval you select, and evaluate the angle of deflection at t by computing:

$$\Theta = \Theta_0 \times \sin\left(\left(\frac{t}{T} \times 360\right) + 90\right)$$

MAKING TRACKS

Carefully enter the program from the flow chart below:

Clear calculator and get into "learn."	OFF-ON [LRN]

When running the program, you'll enter the deflection angle Θ_o at this point.

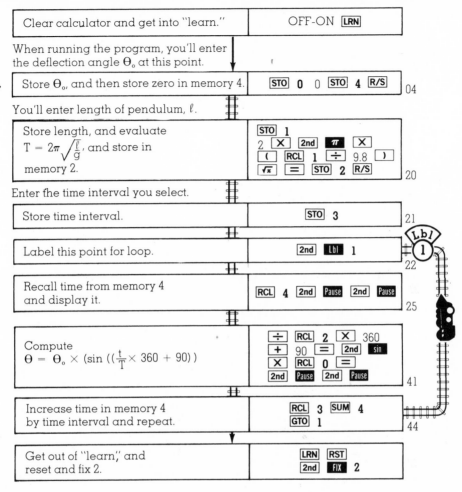

Store Θ_o, and then store zero in memory 4.	[STO] 0 0 [STO] 4 [R/S]	04

You'll enter length of pendulum, ℓ.

Store length, and evaluate $T = 2\pi \sqrt{\frac{\ell}{g}}$, and store in memory 2.	[STO] 1 2 [×] [2nd] [π] [×] ([RCL] 1 [÷] 9.8) [√x] [=] [STO] 2 [R/S]	20

Enter the time interval you select.

Store time interval.	[STO] 3	21

Label this point for loop.	[2nd] [Lbl] 1	22

Recall time from memory 4 and display it.	[RCL] 4 [2nd] [Pause] [2nd] [Pause]	25

Compute $\Theta = \Theta_o \times (\sin ((\frac{t}{T} \times 360 + 90)))$	[÷] [RCL] 2 [×] 360 [+] 90 [=] [2nd] [sin] [×] [RCL] 0 [=] [2nd] [Pause] [2nd] [Pause]	41

Increase time in memory 4 by time interval and repeat.	[RCL] 3 [SUM] 4 [GTO] 1	44

Get out of "learn," and reset and fix 2.	[LRN] [RST] [2nd] [FIX] 2

RUNNING IT

Let's say you would like to watch a pendulum that is 1 meter long, and you originally displace it 15°. (Be sure your calculator is in degree mode.)

PRESS   **DISPLAY/COMMENTS**

		You'll enter the deflection angle
15 [RST] [R/S]	**0.00**	
		You'll enter the length (1 meter).
1 [R/S]	**2.01**	The period (T) is about 2 seconds.

Let's say you select a time interval of 0.2 second.

0.2 [R/S]	**0.00**	Time intervals and angle
	15.00	of swing (Θ) are displayed.
	0.20	(Negative angles indicate
	12.15	pendulum has swung past
	⋮	vertical).

MASS AND RELATIVITY

Einstein's theory of Special Relativity predicts some remarkable phenomena — phenomena which reflect some of the genuine mysteries that are left to unfold as we study nature. One outcome of Einstein's theory predicts the following:

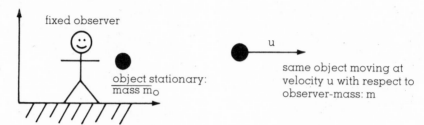

fixed observer

object stationary:
mass m_0

u

same object moving at velocity u with respect to observer-mass: m

If an observer measures the mass of an object while it's stationary with respect to him, he'll measure what Einstein termed the object's "rest mass" — labeled m_0. Einstein's remarkable prediction is that if our observer measures the mass of that same object *while it's moving with respect to him*, he'll measure a *greater mass*. (This remarkable phenomenon predicted by Einstein *has been observed* experimentally.)

The faster the object moves with respect to an observer (the higher the value of u), the greater the measured value of the moving object's mass (m) becomes. The equation that describes this is:

$$m = m_0\left(\frac{1}{\sqrt{1 - (\frac{u}{c})^2}}\right)$$

(mass of   (rest
moving   mass)
object)

In this equation,"c" is the speed of light–a huge number— equal to 3×10^8 meters/sec (or 1.86×10^5 miles/sec). The quantity (c) is the fraction of the speed of light at which an object is moving. For most everyday speeds $(\frac{u}{c})^2$ is so small that the term $\sqrt{1 - (\frac{u}{c})^2}$ never gets much below one — so any increase in mass is not noticed. As "u" gets close to "c", however, the effect gets drastic. We'll write a program that demonstrates this effect. (*Note:* One other prediction of Einstein's work is that no object with a finite rest mass can reach the speed of light with respect to a stationary observer.)

DESTINATION

We'll use your calculator to "take up the speed" and, starting out at ½ the speed of light, increase the velocity of our object and read out what its mass would be at each velocity in steps that approach but never reach the speed of light.

PLANNING THE ROUTE

We'll begin by storing the rest mass and halting. Then begin with a 0.5 in memory zero as the starting value for the object's velocity: ½ the speed of light. Label the next step for a loop that: displays the speed, calls a subroutine that displays the mass, calls a subroutine that steps the velocity, and then repeats. Subroutine 1 is built directly from Einstein's formula for m, Subroutine 2 steps the velocity by half the speed "left" to reach the speed of light.

MAKING TRACKS

Enter the program carefully from the flow chart on the next page.

RUNNING IT

To examine this mass increase in action, watch what happens for a particle with a rest mass (m_o) of 1 gram:

PRESS	DISPLAY/COMMENTS
1 [RST] [R/S]	**1.** m_o entered
[R/S]	**0.5** at 0.5 c (½ speed of light)
	1.1547005 mass about 1.15 gms
	0.75 at .75 c
	1.5118579 mass about 1.5 gm — at ¾ the speed of light, the mass has increased 50%.
	0.875
	2.0655911
	⋮

Note: When the speed reaches .99999999 times the speed of light, your calculator rounds the display to 1, but keeps on computing with its 11 place internal accuracy. It will eventually round to one internally and a flashing 9.9999999 99 will result. Press [CLR] and [RST] to rerun.

MAKING TRACKS

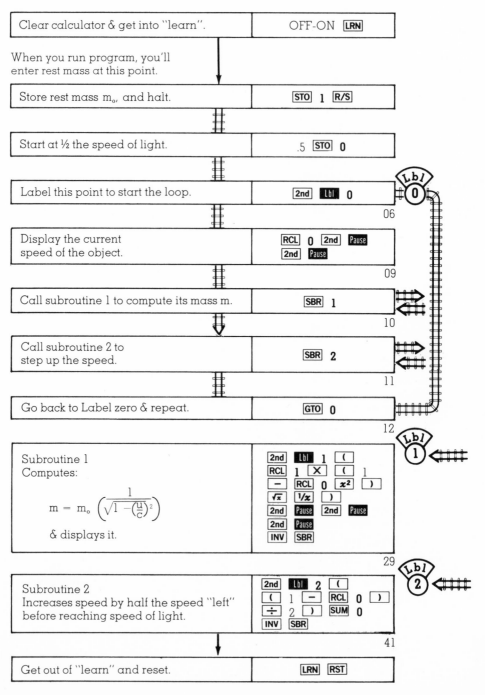

Clear calculator & get into "learn".	OFF-ON [LRN]

When you run program, you'll
enter rest mass at this point.

Store rest mass m_o, and halt.	[STO] 1 [R/S]

Start at ½ the speed of light.	.5 [STO] 0

Label this point to start the loop.	[2nd] [Lbl] 0

06

Display the current speed of the object.	[RCL] 0 [2nd] [Pause] [2nd] [Pause]

09

Call subroutine 1 to compute its mass m.	[SBR] 1

10

Call subroutine 2 to step up the speed.	[SBR] 2

11

Go back to Label zero & repeat.	[GTO] 0

12

Subroutine 1
Computes:

$$m = m_o \left(\frac{1}{\sqrt{1 - \left(\frac{u}{c}\right)^2}} \right)$$

& displays it.

[2nd] [Lbl] 1 [(]
[RCL] 1 [×] [(] 1
[−] [RCL] 0 [x²] [)]
[√x] [1/x] [)]
[2nd] [Pause] [2nd] [Pause]
[2nd] [Pause]
[INV] [SBR]

29

Subroutine 2
Increases speed by half the speed "left"
before reaching speed of light.

[2nd] [Lbl] 2 [(]
[(] 1 [−] [RCL] 0 [)]
[÷] 2 [)] [SUM] 0
[INV] [SBR]

41

Get out of "learn" and reset.	[LRN] [RST]

EXPONENTIAL GROWTH AND DECAY

Many natural phenomena follow a pattern known as exponential growth or decay. When growth or decay depends on the amount of a substance present, this exponential pattern is seen. Bacteria grow at a rate proportional to the number of cells present; radioactive materials decay at a rate proportional to the number of radioactive atoms present. This growth or decay can be predicted by a formula that has the number "e" (base of the natural logs) raised to some exponent:

$$n = n_0 e^{kt} \text{ for "growth"}$$
$$n = n_0 e^{-kt} \text{ for "decay"}.$$

These formulas can be used with test data to determine the constant k, and then used to predict behavior of various natural phenomena. For example, if you know the amount of bacteria present in a colony at one time (number = n_0, at t = 0), and then after a known time t, you measure the number the colony has grown to (n); you can calculate k using the formula:

$$k = \frac{\ln\left(\frac{n}{n_0}\right)}{t}$$

(We're assuming that the bacteria are in growth stage.)

Once k is known, you can use your calculator to "watch" the growth of the bacteria colony as time goes on, calculate the number of bacteria that will be present at a given time, or compute the time at which the specified bacteria count will be reached. (By making k a negative number in your program, it can be used to work with decays, such as radioactive decay.)

DESTINATION

We'll develop a program that consists of several subroutines to handle this situation.

First you'll be able to solve for k by entering test data as follows:
- Enter test value of n_0, press R/S .
- Enter test value of n, press R/S .
- Enter test observation time, t, press R/S .
  At this point k will be displayed.
- To find n for some time t, just enter t and press SBR 1.
- To watch the bacteria "grow" continuously, in time intervals you select, just enter the interval and press SBR 2. The time and bacteria level will be displayed, then the time is increased by the time interval and the new level displayed, etc.
- To find the time at which the bacteria will reach some growth level n, just enter n and press SBR 3.

PLANNING THE ROUTE

This program has four parts:
1) First, it stores n_o in memory 0, n in memory 1, and the test observation time t in memory 2. Then k is calculated and stored in memory 3.
2) Subroutine 1 allows you to enter any t value, and will compute n, using $n = n_o e^{kt}$.
3) Subroutine 2 allows you to enter any time increment; it sums this to the time in memory 4, displays the new time, calculates n using subroutine 1, displays it and then steps and repeats.
4) Subroutine 3 lets you enter a bacteria count, n, and then compute the time needed to reach it using:

$$t = \frac{\ln(\frac{n}{n_o})}{k}$$

MAKING TRACKS

Key in the program carefully from the flow chart on the next page.

RUNNING IT

If you're watching a culture of bacteria that starts with a count of 500, and grows to 1500 after 5 hours:
   a) how many bacteria will be present after 10 hours?
   b) watch this culture "grow" from 10 to 24 hours in one hour increments.
   c) after how many hours will the bacteria count reach 1 million?

PRESS	DISPLAY/COMMENTS
500 [RST] [R/S]	**500.** Enter n_o.
1500 [R/S]	**1500.** Enter observation value, n.
	Enter 5 hour observation time.
5 [R/S]	**0.2197225** k calculated and displayed.
10	**10** Enter 10 hour growth time.
[SBR] 1	**4500.** Bacterial count after 10 hours.
1	**1** Enter 1 hour time increment.
[SBR] 2	**11.** after 11 hours . . .
	5605.7892 Bacterial count
	12. 12 hours.
	6983.3051 Bacterial count
	⋮ ⋮
	24. after 24 hours
[R/S]	**97533.1** Bacterial count (press [R/S] and hold).
[CLR]	**0.** To clear any pending operations.
1 [EE] 6	**1 06** Enter 1 million (1×10^6)
[SBR] 3	**3.4593198 01** hours to grow to count of 1 million (34.6 hours)

MAKING TRACKS

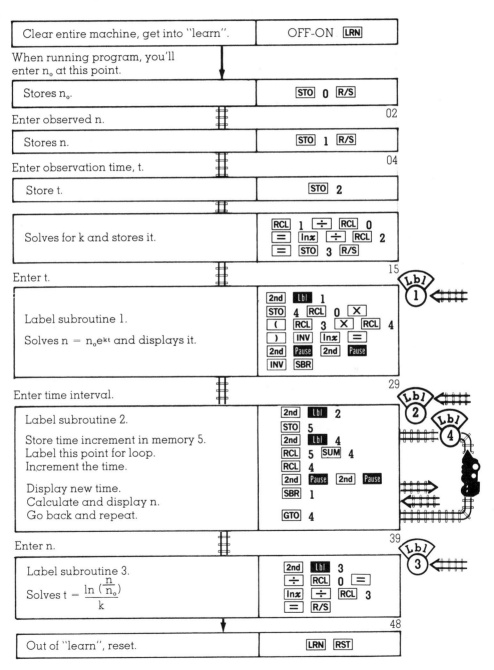

| Clear entire machine, get into "learn". | OFF-ON [LRN] |

When running program, you'll enter n_0 at this point.

| Stores n_0. | [STO] 0 [R/S] |

Enter observed n.   02

| Stores n. | [STO] 1 [R/S] |

Enter observation time, t.   04

| Store t. | [STO] 2 |

| Solves for k and stores it. | [RCL] 1 [÷] [RCL] 0 [=] [Inx] [÷] [RCL] 2 [=] [STO] 3 [R/S] |

Enter t.   15

Lbl 1

Label subroutine 1.

Solves $n = n_0 e^{kt}$ and displays it.

[2nd] [Lbl] 1
[STO] 4 [RCL] 0 [×]
[( ] [RCL] 3 [×] [RCL] 4
[ )] [INV] [Inx] [=]
[2nd] [Pause] [2nd] [Pause]
[INV] [SBR]

Enter time interval.   29

Lbl 2   Lbl 4

Label subroutine 2.

Store time increment in memory 5.
Label this point for loop.
Increment the time.

Display new time.
Calculate and display n.
Go back and repeat.

[2nd] [Lbl] 2
[STO] 5
[2nd] [Lbl] 4
[RCL] 5 [SUM] 4
[RCL] 4
[2nd] [Pause] [2nd] [Pause]
[SBR] 1
[GTO] 4

Enter n.   39

Lbl 3

Label subroutine 3.

Solves $t = \dfrac{\ln\left(\frac{n}{n_0}\right)}{k}$

[2nd] [Lbl] 3
[÷] [RCL] 0 [=]
[Inx] [÷] [RCL] 3
[=] [R/S]

   48

| Out of "learn", reset. | [LRN] [RST] |

RESONANCE

In nature, any standing spring/mass system, such as the one shown in *figure 1*, will oscillate (bob up and down), at a well defined number of cycles per second called its *resonant frequency* (if disturbed). If k is the spring constant (a measure of the spring stiffness) and m is the mass, the resonant frequency is given by the formula:

$$f_{res} = \frac{1}{2\pi} \sqrt{\frac{k}{m}}.$$

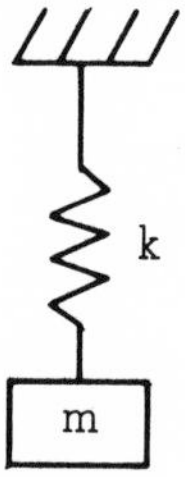

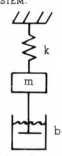

fig. 1
FRICTIONLESS SPRING/
MASS SYSTEM.

fig. 2
SPRING/MASS SYSTEM
WITH DAMPING

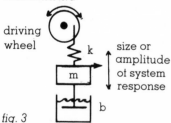

fig. 3
DAMPED SPRING/MASS SYSTEM
WITH PERIODIC "DRIVING FORCE"

Now, if frictional (or "damping") forces are present, this slows things down, and the formula becomes:

$$f'_{res} = \frac{1}{2\pi} \sqrt{\frac{k}{m} - \left(\frac{b}{2m}\right)^2}$$ where b is a

damping constant (describing how strong the damping is.) If any spring/mass system is disturbed in a *periodic way* (with vibrational forces, sound, impulses, etc.), the response of the system will *depend drastically on the frequency of the applied disturbance.*

In *figure 3*, for example, if the driving wheel applies impulses at the *same number of cycles per second* as the system resonant frequency, the maximum system *amplitude* (how far the mass moves in its bobbing) is very great. If the driving force is at much higher or lower frequencies, than the resonant frequency, the system amplitude will be much less. (The actual size of the response also depends on the damping – b. With *no damping* the system amplitude will become infinitely large when the driving frequency equals the resonant frequency – the system destroys itself!)

This program lets you plot how the maximum amplitude of any resonant spring/mass system will vary as the driving frequency of the force is varied. This lets you plot what is called the *resonance response curve* for the system.

The amplitude of the system response is given by:

$$\text{Amplitude} = \frac{F}{\sqrt{m^2\left((2\pi f)^2 - (k/m)^2\right)^2 + b^2\,(2\pi f)^2}}$$

where F is the size of the driving force (in Newtons, N)
  m is the system mass (in kilograms)
  f is the frequency of the driving force in cycles per second (or *hertz*).
  hertz).
  f_{res} is the resonant frequency of the system $= \frac{1}{2\pi}\sqrt{k/m}$

DESTINATION

We'll write a program that evaluates the system's amplitude vs. frequency behavior for a range of frequencies. We'll just store all of the system's important characteristics (or parameters), in the correct units, as follows:

  F — the driving force — in memory 0 (Newtons)
  k — the spring constant — in memory 1 (Newtons/meter)
  m — the system mass — in memory 2 (kilograms)
  b — the damping constant — in memory 3 (Newtons/meters/sec)
  f_{step} — the steps we'll use to increment the driving frequency — in memory 4 (hz)
  f_{start} — the starting point for our driving frequency steps — in memory 5 (hz).

When we press R/S , the calculator will display the driving frequency (in hz), pause, then display the amplitude in meters. The driving frequency will be incremented by f_{step} and the process will loop back & continue with the new driving frequency.

PLANNING THE ROUTE

First, your program will calculate $(\frac{k}{m})$ and store it. Then after a label, recall the current driving frequency which you'll store in memory 5 and display it.

Calculate $(2\pi f)^2$ and store in memory 6. Using the stored values, evaluate the amplitude formula and display it. Step up the driving frequency, and loop back and repeat.

MAKING TRACKS

Enter the program carefully from the flow chart on the following page. Be sure to use the correct units when entering your data.

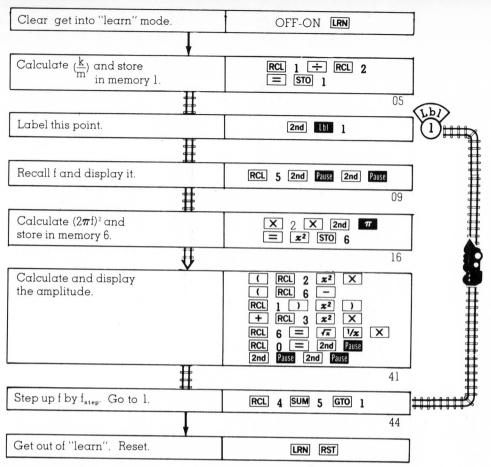

Clear get into "learn" mode.	OFF-ON [LRN]
Calculate $(\frac{k}{m})$ and store in memory 1.	[RCL] 1 [÷] [RCL] 2 [=] [STO] 1

05

Label this point.	[2nd] [Lbl] 1

Recall f and display it.	[RCL] 5 [2nd] [Pause] [2nd] [Pause]

09

Calculate $(2\pi f)^2$ and store in memory 6.	[×] 2 [×] [2nd] [π] [=] [x²] [STO] 6

16

Calculate and display the amplitude.	[(] [RCL] 2 [x²] [×] [(] [RCL] 6 [−] [RCL] 1 [)] [x²] [)] [+] [RCL] 3 [x²] [×] [RCL] 6 [=] [√x] [1/x] [×] [RCL] 0 [=] [2nd] [Pause] [2nd] [Pause] [2nd] [Pause]

41

Step up f by f_{step}. Go to 1.	[RCL] 4 [SUM] 5 [GTO] 1

44

Get out of "learn". Reset.	[LRN] [RST]

RUNNING IT

To display the amplitude vs driving frequency for the system shown:

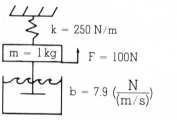

k = 250 N/m

m = 1 kg   F = 100N

b = 7.9 $(\frac{N}{(m/s)})$

$$f_{res} = \frac{1}{2\pi} \sqrt{\frac{k}{m}} = \frac{1}{2\pi} \sqrt{250}$$

2.5164606 hz. (cycles/second)

(You'll see the resonant frequency as the amplitude gets to maximum.)

PRESS	DISPLAY/COMMENTS
[RST]	**0**
100 [STO] **0**	**100** The force F, 100 N
250 [STO] **1**	**250.** The spring constant, k, 250 N/m
1 [STO] **2**	**1.** The system mass, m, 1 kg
7.9 [STO] **3**	**7.9** The damping constant, b, 7.9 $\frac{N}{(m/s)}$
0.25 [STO] **4**	**0.25** The step frequency 0.25 hz
0 [STO] **5**	**0.** The starting frequency:
[R/S]	**0.** frequency
	0.4 amplitude
	0.25 . next frequency
	:

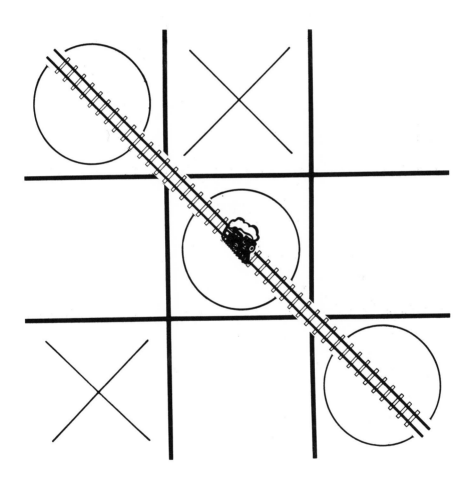

INTRODUCTION

The first time someone picks up a calculator — even a programmable one — what's the first thing they do? Balance a checkbook? Calculate a unit price? Run a program? Not usually. They *play* with it, that's what they do! And it's well that they should. The calculator, as well as being a powerful tool, also qualifies as a great toy. It's one that lets you dabble at mathematical relationships, play "what if" types of games or just see what 12345678×87654321 equals — all instantly.

Programmability adds a new dimension to the recreational side of your calculator, just as it adds to its problem solving power. You can program your calculator to simulate, react, present alternatives, and "play" in a variety of stimulating game situations. In this chapter we'll present a brief selection of the activities and games possible with your calculator. We'll be altering our approach a bit in this section, and presenting the programs involved in a more compact keystroke sequence format. Our object here is to have you *enjoy* the programs — as well as illustrate the type of games possible on your calculator.

We hope you find these activities fun, educational and stimulating — and that they spark you to write a few of your own! The programs we'll be discussing here include:

- **Days of Your Life/Biorhythm:**
  This program enables you to easily calculate the exact number of days you've been alive, and then to "predict" whether you'll have a "good" or "bad" day — according to the theory of "Biorhythm".

- **Dice Toss:**
  Playing a board game that needs a dice toss to get you around the board? Lost your dice? This program will let your calculator fill in for games of chance.

- **On Target:**
  Target practice with a cannon! Can you hit the target in fewer shots than your opponent?

- **Day of the Week:**
  Ever want to know what day of the week it was for some date in the past? This program tells you that it was a Thursday on July 4, 1776, your grandmother was born on a Saturday, etc.

- **Hi-Lo:**
  A number guessing and strategy game — with the calculator giving clues. Try your luck!

- **Ghost Ship:**
  You're trying to sink an "enemy" ship with 7 "wide range" missiles. Can you do it?

DAYS OF YOUR LIFE/ BIORHYTHM

The Theory of Biorhythm states that there are 3 "cycles" to your life, each of which started on the day you were born:

The Physical Cycle: 23 days long
The Emotional Cycle: 28 days long
The Intellectual Cycle: 33 days long

The "cycles" can be expressed as numbers that vary from plus one to minus one. Days when the cycles are near +1 are considered to be "up" or "good" days, and days near −1 are "down" days. Days when a cycle is near 0 are said to be "critical" days. The cycles are shown in the picture below:

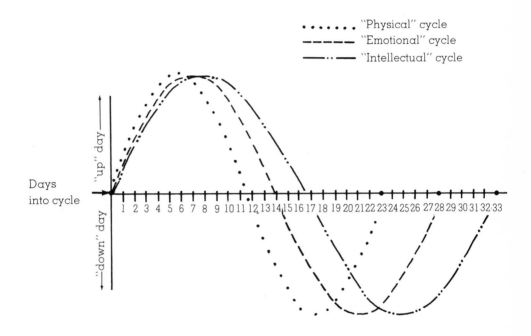

Your programmable calculator will let you easily compute the approximate biorhythm cycles for you and your friends. Also, along the way you'll find out how many days you've been alive.

MAKING TRACKS

Key in the program directly from the Biorythm keystroke chart shown. The key codes are provided for you to check on the program if needed.

Biorythm

KEY	LOC	CODE	KEY	LOC	CODE
OFF-ON [LRN]			3	23	03
[X]	00	55	[SBR] 1	24	61 1
3	01	03	[RCL] 1	25	33 1
6	02	06	[÷]	26	45
5	03	05	2	27	02
[.]	04	83	8	28	08
2	05	02	[SBR] 1	29	61 1
5	06	05	[RCL] 1	30	33 1
[=]	07	85	[÷]	31	45
[2nd] [Int]	08	49	3	32	03
[+]	09	75	3	33	03
1	10	01	[SBR] 1	34	61 1
[=]	11	85	[2nd] [Lbl] 1	35	86 1
[STO] 1	12	32 1	[=]	36	85
[R/S]	13	81	[INV] [2nd] [Int]	37	−49
[2nd] [Lbl] 0	14	86 0	[X]	38	55
[SUM] 1	15	34 1	3	39	03
[R/S]	16	81	6	40	06
[INV] [2nd] [x=t]	17	−66	0	41	00
[GTO] 0	18	51 0	[=]	42	85
[RCL] 1	19	33 1	[2nd] [sin]	43	28
[R/S]	20	81	[R/S]	44	81
[÷]	21	45	[INV] [SBR]	45	−61
2	22	02	[LRN] [RST]		

To Use the Program

Here's how you use the program:
- Enter your age and press [RST] [R/S]
- Next, use the following chart (and steps a through d below) to enter the number of days from your last birthday to today.

a) First enter the number of days after your birthday in the month you were born and press [R/S].

Number of Days in Each Month

Jan 31	April 30	July 31	Oct 31
Feb 28 (29)	May 31	Aug 31	Nov 30
Mar 31	June 30	Sept 30	Dec 31

b) Then enter the number of days in each month following your birth month up to this month, pressing [R/S] after each entry.
(In leap years, February has 29 days.)

c) Enter today's date (1 through 31), press [R/S].

d) Enter 0 and press [R/S] to end the "counting days" routine.

The display now shows the total days you've been alive.
- Press [R/S] to see where your physical cycle is.
- Press [R/S] again to see your emotional cycle.
- Press [R/S] again to see your intellectual cycle.

Again a number close to +1 shows "up" or good for that cycle, a number close to −1 is "down" — a number close to zero is critical! Have a good day!

RUNNING IT

Let's say you were born on July 25th, 1959 and you're checking your biorythm for March 15, 1977.

PRESS	DISPLAY/COMMENTS	
2nd FIX 2	**0.00**	Now, enter your age and press RST R/S .
17 RST R/S	**6210.00**	This is the number of days in the "whole" years you've lived. Now add the number of days since your last birthday. If you were born on July 25, the number of days left in July is 31 − 25 or 6
6 R/S	**6.00**	
	Enter days in August	
31 R/S	**31.00**	
	Sept	
30 R/S	**30.00**	
	Oct	
31 R/S	**31.00**	
	Nov	
30 R/S	**30.00**	
	Dec	
31 R/S	**31.00**	
	Jan	
31 R/S	**31.00**	
	Feb	
28 R/S	**28.00**	
	Now add the date of this month (March 15)	
15 R/S	**15.00**	
	Enter 0 to tell the calculator that's all.	
0 R/S	**6443.00**	You've been alive 6,443 days.
R/S	**0.73**	Your physical cycle is pretty good.
R/S	**0.62**	Your emotional cycle is also good.
R/S	**1.00**	Your intellectual cycle is very high.

March 15, 1977 (according to biorhythm theory) should have been a good day for those born on July 25, 1959.

DICE TOSS

Many board games require a toss of the dice as part of the play. But dice are pesky things — let's say you can't find them. (Or how about a game while out camping — or in the car where it's difficult to roll them?) Well, here's a program that lets your calculator "fill in" as a pair of dice.

To "Roll" the Dice:

This program is designed to simulate rolling dice and give you a number from 2 to 12 each time you "roll" the dice. All you'll have to do is:

- Enter a starting number (less than one). For example, press ⌐·⌐ and enter the number of the month, the day of the month and the time (this will give a variety of starting numbers for repeated use). Then press R/S .
- To roll the dice, just press R/S and you'll first see the value of each die (one at a time with a pause) and then you'll see the total of the two.
- To roll again, just push R/S .

Making Tracks

Key in the program using the *Dice Toss* keystroke chart. (Don't forget OFF-ON and LRN .)

Running It

Press	Display/Comments
RST ⌐·⌐ 412525 R/S	**0.412525** Say you use April 12 at 5:25 for a starting number. (Anything less than 1 works.)
R/S	**5.** 1st digit (pause)
	4. 2nd digit (pause)
	9. Sum of 2
R/S	**2.**
	4. 2nd roll
	6.
	•
	•
	etc.

Dice Toss

KEY		LOC	CODE
OFF-ON [LRN]			
[STO] 0		00	32 0
[R/S]		01	81
[2nd] [Lbl] 1		02	86 1
[SBR] 9		03	61 9
[STO] 1		04	32 1
[SBR] 9		05	61 9
[SUM] 1		06	34 1
[RCL] 1		07	33 1
[R/S]		08	81
[GTO] 1		09	51 1
[2nd] [Lbl] 9		10	86 9
[2nd] [π]		11	30
[+]		12	75
[RCL] 0		13	33 0
[=]		14	85
[yˣ]		15	35
8		16	08
[−]		17	65
[2nd] [Int]		18	49
[=]		19	85
[STO] 0		20	32 0
[×]		21	55
6		22	06
[+]		23	75
1		24	01
[=]		25	85
[2nd] [Int]		26	49
[2nd] [Pause]		27	36
[2nd] [Pause]		28	36
[INV] [SBR]		29	−61
[LRN] [RST]			

ON TARGET

This game puts you "in command" of a cannon that has a range of 1000-40,000 meters. You or your opponent first chooses a target distance that falls somewhere within that range. After the target distance is chosen, you (or your opponent) select an angle of elevation for the cannon between 0° and 90°, and fire! (Don't use 90° or you'll blow up the cannon!) The calculator will flash 9.9999999 if you score a "hit" within 100 meters of the target. (Also if you use 90°). If you overshoot, the calculator display shows the positive distance you overshot. If you undershoot you'll see the negative distance that you were short. The calculator keeps track of how many shots you take — the object being to hit the target in as few shots as possible.

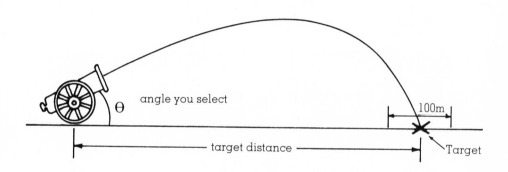

To Play the Game

To play the game, you first enter a target distance between 1000 and 40,000; and press [STO] **3**. Then press [CLR] (if you're playing an opponent) and hand your calculator to your opponent and let him try to hit the target. When he does, push [RCL] **4** to see how many shots it required for him to home in on it. Then, your opponent enters a target distance and you try to score a hit with fewer shots.

Making Tracks

Key in the program carefully from the *On Target* keystroke list. Don't forget to turn your calculator OFF-ON, and then press [LRN] at the start and [LRN] at completion.

On Target

KEY		LOC	CODE
OFF/ON	[LRN]		
[STO]	0	00	32 0
1		01	01
[SUM]	4	02	34 4
8		03	08
0		04	00
0		05	00
0		06	00
0		07	00
[STO]	1	08	32 1
[RCL]	0	09	33 0
[2nd]	tan	10	20
[×]		11	55
[RCL]	0	12	33 0
[2nd]	cos	13	29
[x²]		14	23
[×]		15	55
[RCL]	1	16	33 1
[=]		17	85
[STO]	2	18	32 2

KEY		LOC	CODE
1		19	01
0		20	00
0		21	00
[x:t]		22	22
[RCL]	2	23	33 2
[−]		24	65
[RCL]	3	25	33 3
[=]		26	85
[2nd]	|x|	27	40
[2nd] [INV]	x≥t	28	−76
[GTO]	1	29	51 1
[RCL]	2	30	33 2
[−]		31	65
[RCL]	3	32	33 3
[=]		33	85
[R/S]		34	81
[RST]		35	71
[2nd] Lbl	1	36	86 1
[CLR]		37	15
[1/x]		38	25
[LRN] [RST]			

RUNNING IT

Here's an example of how play might go with 20,000 entered as the target distance.

PRESS	DISPLAY/COMMENTS
20,000 [STO] 3	**20000.** Enter distance to target.(Press [CLR].) Then try various angles until you get a hit.
40 [RST] [R/S]	**19392.31** You overshot by 19392.31 meters.
22 [R/S]	**7786.3348** Overshot.
12 [R/S]	**−3730.5343** Undershot.
15 [R/S]	**9.9999999 99** You scored a hit.
[CLR]	Stops the flashing display.
[RCL] 4	**4.** It took 4 shots for you to score a hit.

To play again, press [CLR] [INV] [2nd] **C.t** and reload and fire as above.

DAY OF THE WEEK

Have you ever wondered, "On what day of the week was I born?" Here is a program that will give you the result you want (for any date using the Gregorian calendar for the years from 1582 through the year 1999). *Note:* The English-speaking countries, including the U.S., did not adopt the Gregorian calendar until 1752.

To Use the Program:

To find the day of the week you'll need to consider several things. Since a calculator can only accept numbers from you as input, you'll need to code the date, following the rules we'll describe. This program requires 4 codes for any date: one for the month, one for the day, one for the first two digits of the year and the last for the last 2 digits of the year. Let's look at each of these.

- *First,* you'll enter the number code for the month using this chart. (*Note:* it starts with March as 1, April as 2 . . .) and push STO 1.

March	*1*
April	*2*
May	*3*
June	*4*
July	*5*
August	*6*
Sept.	*7*
Oct.	*8*
Nov.	*9*
Dec.	*10*
Jan.	*11*
Feb.	*12*

- *Second,* you'll enter the day of the month and push STO 2.
- *Third,* enter the first two digits of the year and press STO 3.
- *Fourth,* you'll enter the last two digits of the year and press STO 4.

Important: If you entered an 11 or 12 for the month (1st entry) then the number representing the year *must* be decreased by 1 before storing.

Finally, push RST R/S and the calculator will give you a one-digit code for the day of the week according to this chart.

Sunday	*0*
Monday	*1*
Tuesday	*2*
Wednesday	*3*
Thursday	*4*
Friday	*5*
Saturday	*6*

MAKING TRACKS

Key in the program using the *Day of the Week* keystroke chart. (Don't forget OFF-ON and LRN .) Since this program has 50 steps, the calculator will automatically leave "learn" when the program is completely entered.

Day of the Week

KEY		LOC	CODE		KEY		LOC	CODE
OFF-ON LRN					4		26	04
RCL 2		00	33 2		−		27	65
+		01	75		2nd Int		28	49
(		02	43		2		29	02
2		03	02		×		30	55
•		04	83		RCL 3		31	33 3
6		05	06		)		32	44
×		06	55		2nd Lbl 0		33	86 0
RCL 1		07	33 1		=		34	85
−		08	65		2nd x≥t		35	76
•		09	83		GTO 1		36	51 1
2		10	02		+		37	75
)		11	44		7		38	07
2nd Int		12	49		GTO 0		39	51 0
+		13	75		2nd Lbl 1		40	86 1
(		14	43		÷		41	45
RCL 4		15	33 4		7		42	07
÷		16	45		=		43	85
4		17	04		INV 2nd Int		44	−49
+		18	75		×		45	55
RCL 4		19	33 4		7		46	07
)		20	44		=		47	85
2nd Int		21	49		2nd Int		48	49
+		22	75		R/S		49	81
(		23	43					
RCL 3		24	33 3					
÷		25	45					

Running It

Let's try it for July 4, 1776.

PRESS	DISPLAY/COMMENTS
5 STO 1	**5.** code for July.
4 STO 2	**4.** Enter date.
17 STO 3	**17.** 1st two digits of year.
76 STO 4	**76.** 2nd two digits of year.
RST R/S	**4.** July 4, 1776 was a Thursday (4 is code for Thursday).

To run this program for another date, press CLR , and INV 2nd C.t before proceeding.

Note: If Jan. or Feb. used, be sure and reduce year by 1 — i.e., 1732 to 1731, 1700 to 1699, etc. before storing.

11

HI-LO

How many guesses will it take you to discover a "secret" number between 0 and 1023? You'll get a clue after each guess (you're told whether your guess was "high" or "low"). This program makes your calculator a game that's fun to have along on trips in the car, while camping — anywhere.

To Play the Game:

The "Hi-Lo" program uses an initial entry number (less than one) to generate a "secret number" for you to guess. Each time you guess, a plus 1 is displayed if your guess is too large, a minus one is shown if your guess is too small, or the secret number is flashed if you guess correctly. After you key in the program, you'll follow these steps:

- Press ⦿ , then enter the time of the day, the number of the month, and the day of the month. (This gives a convenient starting number less than 1.) Now press R/S . At this point, your calculator "knows" its secret number; and it displays a zero — telling you it's ready to play.
- Now try to guess the number by entering your guess and pressing SBR 4. If your guess is "Hi" a 1 is displayed; if low, a −1 is shown. If you guess right, the secret number flashes.
- To guess again, enter your new number and press SBR 4.
- After you've guessed correctly, press RCL 1 to see the number of guesses! To play again, press CLR to stop the flashing and SBR 1 — telling the calculator to create another secret number for you to guess. Then, just enter your number, press SBR 4 and "guess away".

Making Tracks

Key in the program using the *Hi-Lo* keystroke chart. (Don't forget OFF-ON and LRN .)

Hi-Lo

KEY		LOC	CODE		KEY		LOC	CODE
OFF-ON	LRN				STO 7		23	32 7
STO 0		00	32 0		CLR		24	15
2nd Lbl 1		01	86 1		R/S		25	81
0		02	00		2nd Lbl 4		26	86 4
STO 1		03	32 1		STO 2		27	32 2
2nd π		04	30		1		28	01
+		05	75		SUM 1		29	34 1
RCL 0		06	33 0		RCL 2		30	33 2
=		07	85		INV 2nd x≥t		31	−76
yˣ		08	35		GTO 8		32	51 8
8		09	08		2nd x=t		33	66
−		10	65		GTO 7		34	51 7
2nd Int		11	49		1		35	01
=		12	85		=		36	85
STO 0		13	32 0		R/S		37	81
×		14	55		2nd Lbl 8		38	86 8
1		15	01		1		39	01
0		16	00		+/−		40	84
2		17	02		=		41	85
3		18	03		R/S		42	81
+		19	75		2nd Lbl 7		43	86 7
1		20	01		RCL 7		44	33 7
=		21	85		GTO 3		45	51 3
2nd Int		22	49		LRN RST			

RUNNING IT

Here's how a typical game might go:

PRESS	DISPLAY/COMMENTS
	Enter random number (less than 1) of your choice.
.243411 RST	
R/S	**0** Secret number ready.
500 SBR 4	**1.** Guess too high.
250 SBR 4	**−1.** Guess too low.
400 SBR 4	**−1.** Guess too low.
450 SBR 4	**−1.** Too low.
475 SBR 4	**1.** Too high.
470 SBR 4	**1.** Too high.
466 SBR 4	**466.** Flashing — you're right.
CLR RCL 1	**7.** It took 7 tries.

To use again, press CLR SBR 1. Then enter your guess, press SBR 4 and you're going again.

GHOST SHIP

Here's a great game for two players! You're the captain of the submarine Seamos and your mission is to destroy the mysterious "ghost ship", the Dragoon (your opponent) before it plunders any more of your vessels on the high seas. You're armed with powerful missiles, but your sub only carries seven of them. To knock out the Dragoon and score a "hit", you must explode one missile within 7 miles of it. All you have to go on are reports that affirm that the Dragoon is somewhere at a range of 10 to 100 miles; and between the angles of 0 and 90° on your chart.

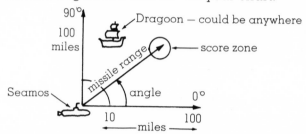

To help you locate the culprit, your ship's sonar will tell you how close each of your missiles came to hitting the Dragoon. With each shot you'll know the distance you missed — and you can use this to help you guess the range and angle for your next shot. If you hit the Dragoon, the distance your missile landed from it will flash (less than 7) and you've succeeded. If you run out of missiles, the number 99999999 99 will flash indicating you lost and the Dragoon's up to its dirty tricks again. Watch out!

To Play the Game:

This is a program for 2 players. The first player enters the range and angle of the Dragoon (unknown to the second) and the second player then tries to hit the Dragoon. Then the players reverse, each trying to hit the Dragoon in fewer shots than the other.

Here's how to use the program:
- Your opponent secretly hides the Dragoon by storing a distance (between 10 and 100) in memory 0 and a direction (between 0° and 90°) in memory 1.
- Then your opponent pushes CLR and hands you the calculator.
- You have 7 shots. To fire, enter the distance, press RST R/S ; and then the angle and press R/S . The display gives the distance you missed (or flashing less than 7 miles for a hit). Continue this firing until you hit the Dragoon or run out of missiles. Good luck!

If you hit the Dragoon, press CLR RCL 4 to see how many shots it took.

To play the game again, press INV 2nd C.t , store a new location in memories 0 and 1 and fire away.

MAKING TRACKS

Key in the program from the *Ghost Ship* keystroke chart. (Don't forget OFF-ON and LRN .)

Ghost Ship

KEY		LOC	CODE	KEY		LOC	CODE
OFF/ON LRN				x^2		21	23
STO 2		00	32 2	+		22	75
R/S		01	81	RCL 2		23	33 2
STO 3		02	32 3	x^2		24	23
7		03	07	=		25	85
x⇄t		04	22	√x		26	24
1		05	01	STO 5		27	32 5
SUM 4		06	34 4	2nd x⇄t		28	76
RCL 3		07	33 3	GTO 1		29	51 1
−		08	65	+		30	75
RCL 1		09	33 1	+		31	75
=		10	85	2nd Lbl 1		32	86 1
2nd COS		11	29	RCL 4		33	33 4
×		12	55	2nd x⇄t		34	76
RCL 0		13	33 0	GTO 2		35	51 2
×		14	55	RCL 5		36	33 5
RCL 2		15	33 2	R/S		37	81
×		16	55	2nd Lbl 2		38	86 2
2		17	02	0		39	00
+/−		18	84	1/x		40	25
+		19	75	LRN			
RCL 0		20	33 0	RST			

RUNNING IT

Here's how a typical game might proceed:

PRESS	DISPLAY/COMMENTS
	First player hides the "Dragoon".
75 STO 0	**75.** Distance to Dragoon.
23 STO 1	**23.** Angle to Dragoon.
CLR	**0** Now give to opponent.
50 RST R/S	**50.** 1st guess is 50 miles.
45 R/S	1st angle is 45.
	34.221646 You missed by over 34 miles.
75 RST R/S	**75.**
45 R/S	**28.621349** 2nd shot missed
50 RST R/S	**50.**
22.5 R/S	**25.005711** 3rd shot missed
75 RST R/S	**75.**
22.5 R/S	**0.6544929** Flashing — a hit!
CLR RCL 4	**4.** It took 4 shots

A LOOK INSIDE: THE HISTORY AND TECHNOLOGY OF YOUR CALCULATOR
12

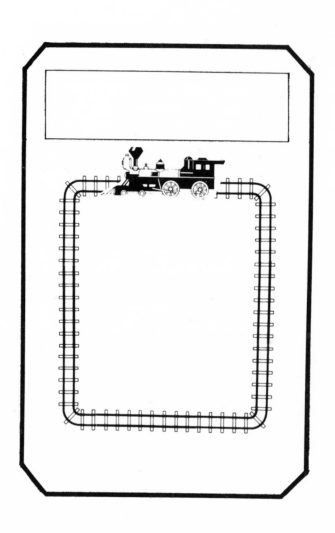

INTRODUCTION

Your calculator represents one "link" in what has been, and undoubtedly will continue to be, an explosive evolution in technology. As you become more familiar with some of its amazing features, you may wonder about such questions as: "How did it get here, how is it built, and just what goes on inside anyway?" In this chapter, we'll try to take a look at the answers to some of these questions — and give you a quick review of the story of your calculator. (By the way, this chapter is strictly optional reading — for those who may be curious about calculator operations. We won't cover any "how to use" information here.)

EARLY CALCULATING DEVICES

The beginning of the story of any calculator goes back quite awhile — into the origins of mathematics itself. People using mathematics realized quite early that there were some parts of math that were a lot more fun to use than others. Getting to the answer involved not only looking carefully at nature and people and analyzing them (fun part), but also involved adding, subtracting, multiplying, dividing and remembering very cumbersome numbers (not so much fun part). People searched for tools that would handle the arithmetic part of mathematics more easily, quickly, and accurately.

What historians usually consider to be the first calculating device is the abacus, which originated in the Orient more than 5000 years ago (and is still in widespread use today). The abacus is a number storage and manipulation device, that some folks can use to compute with great speed and accuracy. It consists of a parallel row of wires, grooves or rods on which small markers — beads or blocks — can be strung and manipulated. The abacus began what was at first a rather slow calculator evolution.

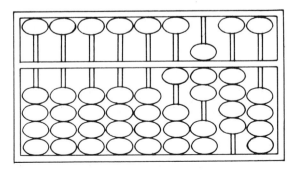

This evolution picked up some speed in 1617 when the Scotch mathematician, John Napier, published a paper which described how multiplication and division could be handled rapidly with the aid of specially marked "rods". (These rods were carved out of ivory — and are usually referred to as "Napier's Bones".) Napier's "rods" and his work in mathematics laid the groundwork for the development of the slide rule — which up until the advent of the inexpensive hand calculator, was widely used in handling complex computations.

The first actual "adding machine", having a resemblance to the mechanical desk calculators popular a few years ago, was invented by the French scientist and philosopher, Blaise Pascal, in 1642.

It was a complex entanglement of wheels, gears and windows, which enabled him to speed up the handling of his father's business accounts. This led the way to the development of a more advanced machine in the late 1600's by Gottfried Leibnitz, called the "Stepped Reckoner". Leibnitz' instrument could not only add, but could also multiply, divide, and extract square roots. (Leibnitz' machine used a sequence of computations for extracting roots that's quite similar to the sequence used in many computers and calculators today.) Early attempts at manufacturing calculators, however, produced highly unreliable results. It was not until 1820 that the first commercial machines handling the operations of addition, subtraction, multiplication and division became available.

DEVELOPMENT OF COMPUTERS: THE PUNCHED CARD

The next major breakthrough in calculator and computer evolution occurred during the early 1800's, and had several authors. One primary innovator was a French inventor named Joseph Marie Jacquard, who invented a self-controlled loom for weaving cloth. The Jacquard loom was controlled by punched cards, which stored data and instructions in code for each loom operation. Jacquard's brainchild — the idea of punched card storage — was then incorporated in a novel machine invented by Charles Babbage in England (1835). Babbage's invention used punched cards to store numbers to be worked with, *and* operations to be performed with them. It was the first "programmable" computing device. It could run through a series of prewritten operations, use results of one computation as input data for another, and handle repetitive calculations or "loops".

Babbage's invention is probably best known, however, for being the first machine to handle *conditional transfers*. As in your calculator, the "Analytical Engine" could compare two numbers, and — depending on the results, transfer to various instruction sequences. The results of one calculation could be used to change numbers and instructions previously set into the machine. Babbage's visionary work was a milestone in the evolution of today's calculators and computers.

Electricity was pressed into the data processing service when Herman Hollerith, an American statistician, used punched cards and electrical reading equipment in helping to take the 1890 U.S. Census. Hollerith's innovations helped cut the time needed for classifying and tallying the census data down to one third of its former "by hand" time — and credits him as a primary developer of modern computers. Hollerith went on to set the foundations for the Computing Tabulating Recording Company, which later evolved into International Business Machines (IBM).

Work in the 1900's turned to more and more application of electricity to computation. Early work by Howard Aiken and others at Harvard University, beginning in 1939, resulted in the first fully automatic calculator — dubbed the Harvard Mark I. It was a huge device that was sequenced or "programmed" by punched paper tape. Input data then went in on punched cards and results were recorded on cards with an electric typewriter. The device was about 50 feet long and 8 feet high, and could perform the 4 basic operations plus math table references, to an accuracy of 23 decimal digits.

"All Electronic" Computers

A more rapid calculator and computer revolution was now underway — following the rapid developmental trends in electronic technology. The first all purpose, all electronic digital computer was completed in 1946 at the University of Pennsylvania. It was called the ENIAC, and was developed by J. Presper Eckert and John W. Mauchly. It was the first machine to take advantage of the speed made possible by all electronic calculation — and operated at speeds more than 1000 times faster than its electromechanical counterparts. Eckert and Mauchly went on to develop further computers, and were instrumental in the development of the BINAC and Univac I computers.

Early computers were still not as flexible as modern machines, and another major step in the direction of flexibility in programming came through the efforts of John Von Neumann, working at the Institute for Advanced Study in Princeton, New Jersey. In a landmark paper "Preliminary Discussion of the Logical Design of an Electronic Computing Instrument", Von Neumann and others reviewed the entire field of automatic computation, and presented early designs for a *stored program* computer. Their work had a major impact on computer designs that followed.

The Integrated Circuit

As computer technology began its most rapid phases of growth, it was naturally spurred on by the rapid growth of solid state electronics. The transistor, replacing the vacuum tube in calculating devices and computers, cut down on size and cost,and increased reliability. Transistor machines were a major step in computer advancement and transistor technology in turn led the way to a further breakthrough — the breakthrough that pointed the way to handheld programmable machines.

In the late 1950's scientists at Texas Instruments were working on a device that put complete electronic circuits — including transistors, diodes, capacitors, resistors and their required interconnections, on a single tiny "chip" of silicon. This type of device is called an Integrated Circuit, or "IC" and was invented by Jack Kilby at Texas Instruments in 1958.

Integrated circuits are built using a variety of techniques which resemble a photographic development process. The basic substance on which they are built is a very high purity silicon, grown via a special process into single crystals that are cylindrical in shape (about three inches in diameter — typically over one foot long.) These crystals are "sliced" into wafer thin slices, and many integrated circuits can be built on each slice. The various functional layers needed for circuit operation are built up one at a time using a method which employs a photographic "mask" of the circuit layer to be built, special photosensitive materials to coat the slice during fabrication, acid etching solutions, and special diffusion techniques.

Integrated circuits bring the advantages of small size, reliability, and extreme cost savings to the computational machine. A typical integrated circuit can have the equivalent of 10,000 transistors operational in it. Integrated circuit development, including those devices utilizing the Metal-Oxide Semiconductor Field Effect Transistor (MOSFET), continued on through the 1960's, and was a key factor in making handheld portable calculators a reality.

At the same time integrated circuits were rapidly developing, other breakthroughs were being made in *display* technology. Solid-state displays based on the Gallium Arsenide (GaAs) diode became available in the late 60's. These easy-to-read, relatively low power, high reliability displays were a natural match to the processing capability available in Integrated Circuit "chips". In 1972 Texas Instruments put these IC and display technologies together and introduced its first four-function calculators. These first units sold for $149.95 and were the result of work that began as early as 1965. (TI holds a patent on the Integrated Circuit calculator that dates back to 1967.)

THE "SOAP" BAR

IC technology has undergone explosive growth during the 1970's with more powerful and efficient IC's becoming available at ever reducing costs. With increased experience in building a device, driven by a steadily rising volume of production, the costs for manufacturing can be brought down predictable curves known as "Learning Curves". In the highly competitive consumer electronics industry — these savings (and added benefits) have in large part been passed directly on to you, the consumer. As a result, the mid 1970's have seen the advent of low cost scientific and technical calculators, and today's low cost programmables.

One such single IC chip is the heart and brain of your calculator. This device represents the very latest state of the art development in MOS IC's, incorporating the equivalent of over 30,000 MOSFET's on a single rectangular silicon chip less than ¼ of an inch on each side. Due to its architecture, this chip is called the "Serially Organized Arithmetic Processor", or "SOAP" Bar for short. It's quite a remarkable device, handling all of the juggling necessary to receive keyboard inputs, operate the display, handle complex keyboard calculations, as well as learn and remember the program steps you teach it. The SOAP bar is a major step forward in IC technology and developers used new and very stringent "rules of the game" to achieve this highly innovative design. It's a very "dense" device, cramming more transistors into smaller spaces than conventional IC's. Its "Serial" rather than "Parallel" design eliminates many of the interconnections that normally take up room on an IC chip, so mofe functions can be put on it. ("Serial" means that many numbers and operations are handled inside the chip one *after* another "bit by bit", rather than with many functions and pieces of numbers being handled all at once — which is termed "parallel" design.)

Because of the power and complexity of this single chip, the inside of your calculator can be made highly rugged and reliable — and deceptively simple to look at. Basically there's just the SOAP bar, the keyboard, a display unit, a small printed circuit board, the power supply, and a battery pack. This low number of parts is a major factor leading to low cost, and there's less to go wrong. But, when you turn it on, you're commanding a powerful bundle of technology, ready to solve $2 \times 2 = 4$ or handle complex personal programming problems with equal skill.

WHAT GOES ON INSIDE

The SOAP bar is the "brain" of your calculator and is always active and working while your machine is on — even if it appears to be placidly sitting there with a "0" in the display. The SOAP bar checks for inputs from the keyboard, keeps the display lit up with the correct readout, and handles computations or program steps, all with a tremendous organization and precision.

All of the calculator's tasks are executed with a basic "clock signal", operating at about 1.0 megahertz (that's a clock ticking 1,000,000 times per second!). This means the time interval between some calculator tasks can be as short as 0.000001 seconds. The operations you enter from the keyboard are handled internally by many thousands of calculator tasks, so the time you actually see between a keyboard input and a displayed response may be the good part of a second for some direct calculations — and can be very long for extended looping programs.

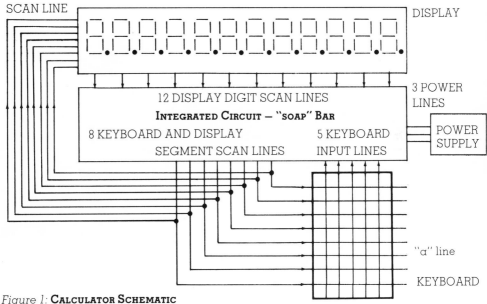

Figure 1: **CALCULATOR SCHEMATIC**

Figure 1 is a simplified schematic diagram of the inside of your calculator, showing the Display, the "SOAP" bar, the Keyboard and the Power Supply. A remarkable thing about the SOAP bar is that for all its power, it's connected to the outside world by only 30 connections. If you consider all of the things the chip has to handle, and all of the information it processes, 30 connections is really a very small number. Let's briefly examine how this works.

THE DISPLAY

Let's say for a moment that your calculator is just sitting there with a **"2."** in the display — waiting for your next command. What's it doing? Well, it's keeping that 2 turned on in the display through a technique called "segment scan"; and also checking the keyboard for your next move. Here's how the segment scan operation works. Each number in your display (display digit) is made up of 8 *Light Emitting Diodes* (LED's). These are special devices that emit light when electric current is passed through them. The 7 segments needed to make each of the numbers, 0 through 9, plus an 8th segment for the decimal point, are designated "a" through "h", as shown in *figure 2*.

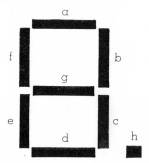

Figure 2

There are 8 "wires" coming from the SOAP bar — called *segment scan lines*, each of which has a dual function. First of all, each scan line is responsible for lighting *all* of the segments of any one type. For example, when the drive voltage is "turned on" in the "a" segment line, it goes to all of the "a" segments. (In all 12 digits on the display, all segments of any one type are connected together. All the a's connect to all other a's, b's to b's, etc.)

Secondly, each segment scan line runs down to the keyboard and provides keyboard scan input to one whole row of keys. In the case of *your* calculator, the "a" line runs to the 6th row down from the top — the row with the SBR 4 5 6 — keys. If you were pressing any of these 5 keys, current would then be directed to go from the scan line up one of the keyboard input lines, and let the chip know which key you pushed.

Now at this point, you might wonder — if all of the "a" segments of all the display digits are activated at the same time, why don't they all go on at once? And — how does your calculator know which key was pushed? Well, the SOAP bar handles both of these tasks quite well by using the fact that any electrical device needs 2 *connections* to turn it on.

A Look Inside 12

In your calculator's display, as we've said, all of the segments of any one type are wired together. So, when the SOAP bar turns on the "a" segment line, all of the "a" segments get ready to turn on; but one more connection is required to "complete the circuit" before it will actually light up. The SOAP bar handles this second connection with 12 more of its 30 connecting wires. These 12 leads are called *digit* scan lines. *All* of the segments (a-h) of any single digit are activated by one of these lines. So by simultaneously activating one of the 8 segment scan lines, and one of the 12 digit scan lines, the SOAP bar can turn on any segment of any digit in the display. To display a number, the SOAP bar just turns on the proper segments (a-h) for the number and the proper digit scan line (1-12) to put the number in the correct digit place in the display. However, the calculator does not show any digit "all at once". The SOAP bar "builds" the number in the display one segment at a time by turning on the correct segments in rapid sequence. *Figure 3* shows the scan sequence for lighting up a 2, with a decimal point. The SOAP bar will turn on the "a" scan line, and simultaneously turn on only those digits in the display that need an "a" segment. It then goes on through the rest.

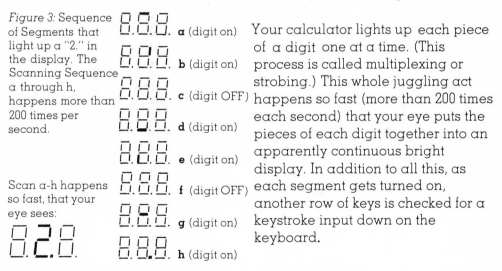

Figure 3: Sequence of Segments that light up a "2." in the display. The Scanning Sequence a through h, happens more than 200 times per second.

Scan a-h happens so fast, that your eye sees:

Your calculator lights up each piece of a digit one at a time. (This process is called multiplexing or strobing.) This whole juggling act happens so fast (more than 200 times each second) that your eye puts the pieces of each digit together into an apparently continuous bright display. In addition to all this, as each segment gets turned on, another row of keys is checked for a keystroke input down on the keyboard.

No matter how fast you press the keys, the scan lines are turned on and off in sequence so fast that one scan will catch you "in the act", and send a current pulse up one of the 5 keyboard input lines. The SOAP bar keeps track of which of the 5 lines the pulse came in on, as well as which scan line was "on" when the pulse came in, and with this "matrix" of information it knows which key you've pressed. So — all of this scanning, keyboard checking, and display lighting happens all the time — whenever your machine is on — even if it's just sitting there.

A SIMPLE CALCULATION

Now, let's consider what happens when you do a simple calculation
[2] [X] [5] [=] , for example. *Figure 4* is a simplified block diagram of the
various features built into the IC chip. With a little patience, you can
follow along with the various processes that go on as your calculator
performs.

- When you press [2] , your keyboard sends a pulse into keyboard
  control circuitry (beginning at point A on the block diagram).This
  circuitry interprets this as a "2" and loads it, via input/output and
  control circuitry, into one of the 4 arithmetic registers (A, B, C, or D) and
  the display control circuitry. Your calculator now displays a 2, and is
  waiting for your next input.

- When you press [X] , the input is received and interpreted by the
  keyboard decode circuitry, and a special signal or *flag* is set up inside
  your calculator — letting it know that a multiplication instruction is to be
  performed.

- When you press [5] , the signal is interpreted as a 5, and a 5 is moved
  into register A and into display control. The 2 is saved in a separate
  math register.

- When you press [=] things really start moving. The flag signal is
  scanned telling the machine, "You need to multiply." The control
  circuitry then goes to the Read Only Memory (ROM), and pulls out the
  instructions necessary to multiply. The 2 and the 5 are then moved to
  the arithmetic logic unit, where they are multiplied together by means
  of a repetitive addition procedure, as controlled by instructions from
  the ROM. The result then gets moved back to register A and the display
  control circuitry — and appears in the display. At this point, the
  calculator is ready for your next instruction.

All of this happens in the wink of an eye — you don't really sit around
waiting very long for the SOAP bar to perform. The basic building block
operations needed to carry out each of your keyboard commands are
stored in the calculator's ROM. The calculator gets the detailed
instructions it needs from the ROM as it goes along — either in response
to keyboard inputs or to instructions it receives from program memory.

For additional reading on how a calculator works, refer to Eugene
McWhorter's excellent article "The Small Electronic Calculator"
(*Scientific American*, March 1976). Note, though, that in this article,
McWhorter describes the operation of a *Digit Scanned* machine — while
your calculator is *segment scanned* as we've mentioned.

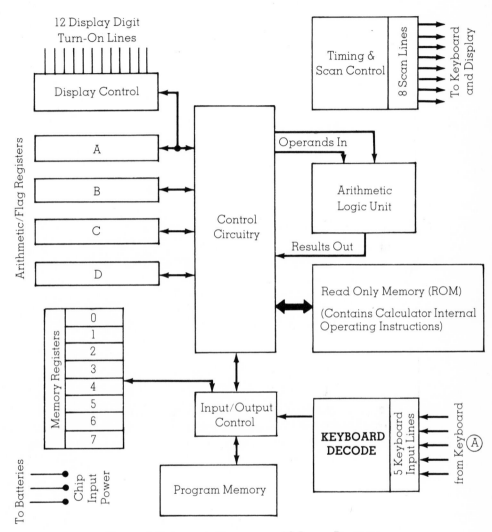

Figure 4: **SIMPLIFIED CALCULATOR IC BLOCK DIAGRAM**

Your programmable calculator represents the latest development
in calculator and IC technology. The costs of bringing you the massive
amounts of logic and memory found in a device like your calculator are
ever decreasing. You'll be seeing more uses and implementation of
programmability in devices for use in your home, at school, for work and
for recreation. Your calculator is a glimpse of this facet of the future —
here today. So enjoy it and explore with it — it's the ideal way to begin
learning about what will become an important part of life through the
next several decades and beyond.

APPENDIX A: BATTERY AND AC OPERATION

NORMAL OPERATION

Your calculator is designed for portable operation with periodic recharging of the battery pack with the adapter/charger supplied. It is important that the proper adapter/charger is used. If replacement of the battery pack or charger becomes necessary, be sure that an exact replacement is obtained.

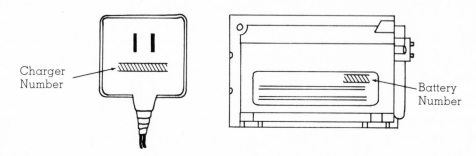

Charger Number

Battery Number

Note: Two different combinations of battery pack and adapter/charger may be used with your calculator. The BP/6 battery pack is used with the AC9131 adapter/charger. The BP/7 battery pack is used with the AC9132 adapter/charger.

Caution: Use of other than the proper Adapter/Charger may apply improper voltage to your calculator and damage the unit.

To ensure maximum portable operating time, connect the Adapter/Charger to a standard 115V/60 Hz outlet, plug into calculator, and charge battery pack at least 4 hours with the calculator OFF or 10 hours with the calculator ON. The adapter/charger and battery pack may become warm when used on AC power. This is normal and of no consequence. (**Caution:** The BP-6 battery pack should only be recharged while properly installed in your calculator.)

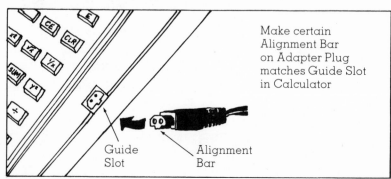

Make certain Alignment Bar on Adapter Plug matches Guide Slot in Calculator

Guide Slot

Alignment Bar

When the battery pack is fully charged, the calculator will operate approximately 2 to 3 hours before recharging is necessary. However, don't hestitate to connect the adapter/charger if you know or suspect the battery pack is nearly discharged. A battery pack near discharge can adversely affect all calculator operations giving erroneous results. A discharged battery pack is typically indicated by a dim, erratic or blank display.

While individual cell life in a battery pack is difficult to predict, under normal use, rechargeable batteries have a life of 2 to 3 years or about 500 to 1000 recharge cycles.

PERIODIC RECHARGING

Although the calculator will operate indefinitely with the adapter/charger connected, the rechargeable battery pack can lose its storage capacity if it is not allowed to discharge occasionally. For maximum battery life, it is recommended that you operate the calculator as a portable at least twice a month, allowing the batteries to discharge, then recharge accordingly.

EXCESSIVE BATTERY DISCHARGING

If the calculator is left on for an extended period of time after the battery pack is discharged (accidentally left on overnight, for example), connect the adapter/charger for at least 24 hours with the calculator OFF. If this does not restore normal battery operation the battery pack should be replaced. Repeated occurrences of excessive battery discharging will permanently damage the battery pack. Spare and replacement battery packs can be purchased directly from Texas Instruments Incorporated, P.O. Box 53, Lubbock, Texas, 79408.

STORAGE

If the calculator is stored or unused for several weeks, the battery pack will probably need recharging before portable use. The battery pack will not leak corrosive material; therefore, it is safe to store the calculator with the battery pack installed.

BATTERY PACK REPLACEMENT

The battery pack can be quickly and simply removed from the calculator. Hold the calculator with the keys facing down. Place a small coin in the slot in the bottom of the calculator. A slight prying motion with the coin will pop the slotted end of the pack out of the calculator. Carefully disconnect the wires that attach the battery pack to the calculator. The pack can then be removed entirely from the calculator.

The metal contacts on the battery pack (where charger and calculator plug in) are the battery terminals. Care should always be taken to prevent any metal object from coming into contact with these terminals and shorting the batteries.

To re-insert the battery pack, first, attach the connecting wires to the terminals of the battery pack. Alignment should not be a problem as the connector will only fit in one position. Then, place the pack into the compartment so that the small step on the end of the pack fits under the edge of the calculator bottom. A small amount of pressure on the battery pack will snap it properly into position. (*Do not force.* It will fit easily when properly oriented.)

APPENDIX B: IN CASE OF DIFFICULTY

In the event that you have difficulty with your calculator, the following instructions will help you to analyze the problem. You may be able to correct your calculator problem without returning it to a service facility. If the suggested remedies are not successful, contact the Consumer Relations Department by mail or telephone (refer to "If You Have Questions or Need Assistance" later in this appendix). Please describe in detail the symptoms of your calculator.

Symptom	Remedy
1. Display is blank for no obvious reason.	Press and hold [R/S] momentarily. If display returns, the calculator was running a long program or operating in a continuous program loop.
	The battery pack may be discharged or improperly installed. Also, check to be sure the ON-OFF switch is fully in the ON position.
2. Display shows erroneous results, flashes erratic numbers, grows dim, or goes blank.	The battery pack is probably discharged or improperly connected. Refer to Battery and AC Operation in appendix A.
3. Display flashes while performing keyboard operations.	An invalid operation or key sequence has been pressed or the limits of the calculator have been violated. See Appendix C for a list of these conditions.

If none of the above procedures corrects the difficulty, return the calculator and charger PREPAID and INSURED to the applicable SERVICE FACILITY.

If the calculator is out of warranty, service rates in effect at time of return will be charged. Please include information on the difficulty experienced with the calculator as well as return address information including name, address, city, state and zip code. The shipment should be carefully packaged, adequately protected against shock and rough handling and sent to one of the Texas Instruments Service Facilities listed with the warranty.

NOTE: The P.O. box number listed for the Lubbock Service Facility is for United States parcel post shipments only. *If you use another carrier, the street address is:*   Texas Instruments Incorporated
2305 University Ave., Lubbock, Texas 79415

CALCULATOR EXCHANGE CENTERS

If your calculator requires service, instead of returning the unit to a service facility for repair, you may elect to exchange the calculator for a factory-rebuilt calculator of the SAME MODEL by going in person to one of the exchange centers which have been established across the United States. A $3.00 charge will be made by the exchange center for in-warranty exchanges. Out-of-warranty exchanges will be charged at the rates in effect at the time of the exchange. Please call the Consumer Relations Department for further details and the location of the nearest exchange center. Do not mail.

IF YOU HAVE QUESTIONS, OR NEED ASSISTANCE OR GENERAL INFORMATION

If you have questions concerning calculator repair, accessory purchase or the basic functions of your calculator, please call our Customer Relations Department at 800-858-1802 (toll free within the contiguous United States except Texas) or 800-692-1353 within Texas.

FOR TECHNICAL ASSISTANCE

For technical questions such as programming, specific calculator applications, etc., you can call 806-747-3841. We regret that this is *not* a toll-free number, and we cannot accept collect calls. As an alternative, you can write to:
Consumer Relations Department
Texas Instruments Incorporated
P.O. Box 53
Lubbock, Texas 79408

Because of the number of suggestions which come to Texas Instruments from many sources containing both new and old ideas, Texas Instruments will consider such suggestions only if they are freely given to Texas Instruments. It is the policy of Texas Instruments to refuse to receive any suggestions in confidence. Therefore, if you wish to share your suggestions with Texas Instruments, or if you wish us to review any calculator program key sequence which you have developed, please include the following statement in your letter:

> "All of the information forwarded herewith is presented to Texas Instruments on a nonconfidential, nonobligatory basis; no relationship, confidential or otherwise, expressed or implied, is established with Texas Instruments by this presentation. Texas Instruments may use, copyright, distribute, publish, reproduce, or dispose of the information in any way without compensation to me."

APPENDIX C: ERROR CONDITIONS

A flashing display indicates that the limits of the calculator have been violated or that an invalid calculator operation has been requested. Pressing CE or CLR stops the flashing. CLR also clears the display and pending operations. CE stops the flashing only, permitting further calculations with undisturbed pending operations. The display flashes for the following reasons:

1. Calculation entry or result (in display or memories) outside the range of the calculator, $\pm 1 \times 10^{-99}$ to $\pm 9.9999999 \times 10^{99}$. The exceeded limit is flashed, indicating underflow or overflow.

2. Inverse of a trigonometric function with an invalid value for the function such as $\sin^{-1}x$ with x greater than 1. The invalid value x is flashed.

3. Root or logarithm of a negative number. The root or logarithm of the absolute value of the number is flashed to indicate the sign error.

4. Raising a negative number to any power (or root). The power (or root) of the absolute value of the number is flashed.

5. Pressing two operation keys in succession. This affects $+$, $-$, $\times$, $\div$, y^x, and INV y^x (for $\sqrt[x]{y}$). The last entered number is flashed.

6. Pressing $=$ or $)$ after $+$, $-$, $\times$, $\div$, y^x, or INV y^x (for $\sqrt[x]{y}$). The last entered number is flashed.

7. Having more than 9 open parentheses or more than 4 pending operations. The 10th parenthesis or 5th operation is not accepted so calculation can continue. The last displayed number is flashed.

8. Dividing a number by zero. "9.9999999 99" is flashed. (Except 0 $\div$ 0 $=$ 1 flashing.)

9. Pressing an operation key before completing any memory operation, fix decimal operation or direct transfer operation. The value in the display is flashed. (i.e. STO $+$)

10. Attempting to store, recall, or use other memory operations with locations other than 0 through 7. (i.e. STO 8).

11. Attempting to find values of functions with entered values outside these limits:

Function	Limit
$\sin^{-1}x$, $\cos^{-1}x$	$-1 \leq x \leq 1$
e^x	$-227.95592 \leq x \leq 230.25850$
10^x	$-99 < x < 100$
$\ln x$	$1 \times 10^{-99} \leq |x| < 1 \times 10^{100}$
$\log x$	$1 \times 10^{-99} \leq x < 1 \times 10^{100}$
INV P→R	$1 \times 10^{+50} < R$

12. Direct transfer instructions (GTO or SBR) that attempt to branch to unassigned label positions. Current display value is flashed. A GTO 2nd **nn** key sequence where **nn** is greater than 49 also produces a flashing condition.
13. Attempting to execute a program past location 49. Current display value is flashed.
14. Attempting to calculate $\bar{x}$ or σ^2 without entering any data or only entering a single data point.

WHEN ERRORS ARE ENCOUNTERED WHEN RUNNING A PROGRAM:

When any of the foregoing errors occur in a program, the program will stop and show you a flashing display. This means you've asked the calculator to do something in a program that it cannot do — even directly from the keyboard.

APPENDIX D: DISPLAYED RESULTS VS ACCURACY

The basic mathematical tolerance of the calculator is controlled by the number of digits it uses for calculations. The calculator appears to use 8 digits as shown by the display, but actually uses 11 digits to perform all calculations. Combined with the built-in 5/4 rounding capability, these extra digits guard the 8-digit display to improve accuracy. Consider the following example in the absence of these guard digits.

$$\frac{1}{3} \times 3 = .99999999 \text{ (inaccurate)}$$

The example shows that $1 \div 3 = .33333333$ when multiplied by 3 produces an inaccurate answer. However, an eleven-digit string of nines will round to 1 when rounded to 8 places.

The higher order mathematical functions use iterative calculations. The cumulative rounding error is usually maintained below the 8-digit display so that no effect can be seen. The three "guard digits" act to protect the display from small cumulative errors.

Normally, there is no need to even consider these guard digits. In certain calculations, however, the guard digits may appear as an answer when not expected. Results of two computations may appear to be equal when shown in the display, but have an inequality in their guard digits. If these two results are subtracted, the calculator may display a nonzero result.

This fact is especially important when writing your own programs. If you're testing a calculated result to be equal to another value, such as with the [2nd] [x=t] instruction, you may need to take precautions to prevent improper evaluation due to the guard digit differences. The key sequence [EE] [INV] [EE] will truncate the guard digits of a result leaving only the rounded display value for further use.

For the standard display, results are accurate for all calculations that do not violate the restrictions listed in Appendix C, except as defined below.

TRIGONOMETRIC FUNCTIONS

All displayed digits are accurate for a $\pm 36,000$ degree range ($\pm 200\,\pi$ radians and $\pm 40,000$ grads). In general, the accuracy decreases one digit for each decade outside this specified accuracy range. An exception is the tangent of an odd multiple of $\pm 90°$, $\pm \pi/2$ radians or ± 100 grads that results in an overflow condition because the function is undefined at these points.

ROOTS AND POWERS

There can be some accuracy loss for roots and powers in calculations when the base (y) gets very close to 1 and the power (x) gets very large.

APPENDIX E: TYPICAL ANSWERS TO "NEXT STOP" PROBLEMS

(*Note:* In general, there is no one "right" program answer to any problem situation. We will show one approach here.)

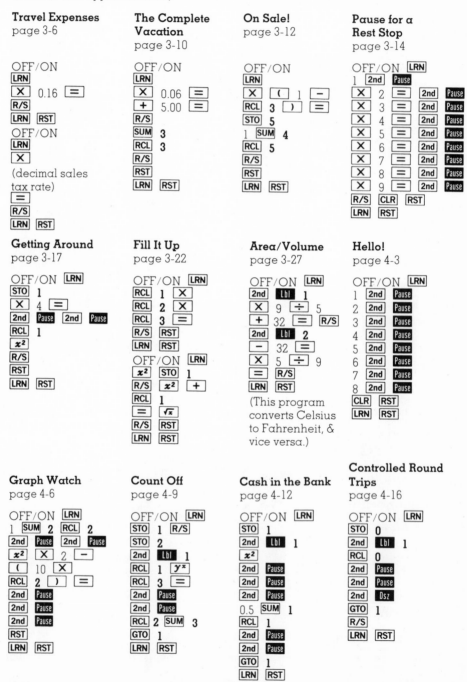

Travel Expenses
page 3-6

OFF/ON
LRN
× 0.16 =
R/S
LRN RST
OFF/ON
LRN
×
(decimal sales tax rate)
=
R/S
LRN RST

The Complete Vacation
page 3-10

OFF/ON
LRN
× 0.06 =
+ 5.00 =
R/S
SUM 3
RCL 3
R/S
RST
LRN RST

On Sale!
page 3-12

OFF/ON
LRN
× (1 −
RCL 3) =
STO 5
1 SUM 4
RCL 5
R/S
RST
LRN RST

Pause for a Rest Stop
page 3-14

OFF/ON LRN
1 2nd Pause
× 2 = 2nd Pause
× 3 = 2nd Pause
× 4 = 2nd Pause
× 5 = 2nd Pause
× 6 = 2nd Pause
× 7 = 2nd Pause
× 8 = 2nd Pause
× 9 = 2nd Pause
R/S CLR RST
LRN RST

Getting Around
page 3-17

OFF/ON LRN
STO 1
× 4 =
2nd Pause 2nd Pause
RCL 1
x²
R/S
RST
LRN RST

Fill It Up
page 3-22

OFF/ON LRN
RCL 1 ×
RCL 2 ×
RCL 3 =
R/S RST
LRN RST
OFF/ON LRN
x² STO 1
R/S x² +
RCL 1
= √x
R/S RST
LRN RST

Area/Volume
page 3-27

OFF/ON LRN
2nd Lbl 1
× 9 ÷ 5
+ 32 = R/S
2nd Lbl 2
− 32 =
× 5 ÷ 9
= R/S
LRN RST

(This program converts Celsius to Fahrenheit, & vice versa.)

Hello!
page 4-3

OFF/ON LRN
1 2nd Pause
2 2nd Pause
3 2nd Pause
4 2nd Pause
5 2nd Pause
6 2nd Pause
7 2nd Pause
8 2nd Pause
CLR RST
LRN RST

Graph Watch
page 4-6

OFF/ON LRN
1 SUM 2 RCL 2
2nd Pause 2nd Pause
x² × 2 −
(10 ×
RCL 2) =
2nd Pause
2nd Pause
2nd Pause
RST
LRN RST

Count Off
page 4-9

OFF/ON LRN
STO 1 R/S
STO 2
2nd Lbl 1
RCL 1 yˣ
RCL 3 =
2nd Pause
2nd Pause
RCL 2 SUM 3
GTO 1
LRN RST

Cash in the Bank
page 4-12

OFF/ON LRN
STO 1
2nd Lbl 1
x²
2nd Pause
2nd Pause
2nd Pause
0.5 SUM 1
RCL 1
2nd Pause
2nd Pause
GTO 1
LRN RST

Controlled Round Trips
page 4-16

OFF/ON LRN
STO 0
2nd Lbl 1
RCL 0
2nd Pause
2nd Pause
2nd Dsz
GTO 1
R/S
LRN RST

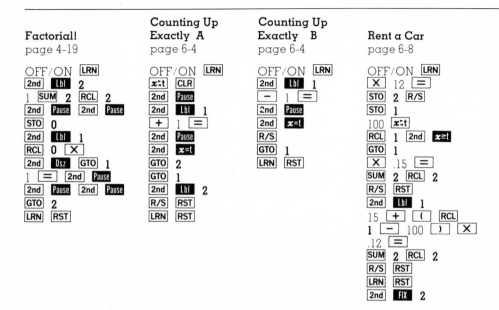

Factorial!
page 4-19

OFF/ON [LRN]
[2nd] [Lbl] 2
1 [SUM] 2 [RCL] 2
[2nd] [Pause] [2nd] [Pause]
[STO] 0
[2nd] [Lbl] 1
[RCL] 0 [×]
[2nd] [Dsz] [GTO] 1
1 [=] [2nd] [Pause]
[2nd] [Pause] [2nd] [Pause]
[GTO] 2
[LRN] [RST]

**Counting Up
Exactly A**
page 6-4

OFF/ON [LRN]
[x⇄t] [CLR]
[2nd] [Pause]
[2nd] [Lbl] 1
[+] 1 [=]
[2nd] [Pause]
[2nd] [x=t]
[GTO] 2
[GTO] 1
[2nd] [Lbl] 2
[R/S] [RST]
[LRN] [RST]

**Counting Up
Exactly   B**
page 6-4

OFF/ON [LRN]
[2nd] [Lbl] 1
[−] 1 [=]
[2nd] [Pause]
[2nd] [x=t]
[R/S]
[GTO] 1
[LRN] [RST]

Rent a Car
page 6-8

OFF/ON [LRN]
[×] 12 [=]
[STO] 2 [R/S]
[STO] 1
100 [x⇄t]
[RCL] 1 [2nd] [x⇄t]
[GTO] 1
[×] .15 [=]
[SUM] 2 [RCL] 2
[R/S] [RST]
[2nd] [Lbl] 1
15 [+] [(] [RCL]
1 [−] 100 [)] [×]
.12 [=]
[SUM] 2 [RCL] 2
[R/S] [RST]
[LRN] [RST]
[2nd] [FIX] 2

Bouncing Ball
page 6-11

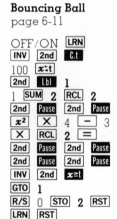

OFF/ON [LRN]
[INV] [2nd] [C.t]
100 [x⇄t]
[2nd] [Lbl] 1
1 [SUM] 2 [RCL] 2
[2nd] [Pause] [2nd] [Pause]
[x²] [×] 4 [−] 3
[×] [RCL] 2 [=]
[2nd] [Pause] [2nd] [Pause]
[2nd] [Pause] [2nd] [Pause]
[INV] [2nd] [x≥t]
[GTO] 1
[R/S] 0 [STO] 2 [RST]
[LRN] [RST]

APPENDIX F: KEY CODES

CALCULATOR KEY CODES – USING ACTUAL KEYBOARD ARRANGEMENT

Rows ↓

	1	2	3	4	5
1	No Code (2nd)	Minus Sign (INV)	log 18 / lnx 13	C.t 19 / CE 14	CLR 15
2	D.MS 26 / LRN (No Code)	P→R 27 / x⇄t 22	sin 28 / x² 23	cos 29 / √x 24	tan 20 / 1/x 25
3	Pause 36 / SST (No Code)	Ins (No Code) / STO 32	Exc 38 / RCL 33	Prd 39 / SUM 34	π 30 / yˣ 35
4	Nop 46 / BST (No Code)	Del (No Code) / EE 42	FIX 48 / (43	Int 49 /) 44	|x| 40 / ÷ 45
5	Dsz 56 / GTO 51	7 07	8 08	9 09	Deg 50 / X 55
6	x=t 66 / SBR 61	4 04	5 05	6 06	Rad 60 / − 65
7	x≥t 76 / RST 71	1 01	2 02	3 03	Grad 70 / + 75
8	Lbl 86 / R/S 81	0 00	Σ+ 88 / · 83	x̄ 89 / +/− 84	σ² 80 / = 85

Columns 1 2 3 4 5
(for → second functions) 6 7 8 9 0

CALCULATOR KEY CODES IN NUMERICAL ORDER

00	0	−27	INV 2nd P→R	50	2nd Deg
01	1	28	2nd sin	51	GTO
02	2	−28	INV 2nd sin	55	X
03	3	29	2nd cos	56	2nd Dsz
04	4	−29	INV 2nd cos	−56	INV 2nd Dsz
05	5	30	2nd π	60	2nd Rad
06	6	32	STO	61	SBR
07	7	33	RCL	−61	INV SBR
08	8	34	SUM	65	−
09	9	−34	INV SUM	66	2nd x=t
13	lnx	35	yˣ	−66	INV 2nd x=t
−13	INV lnx	−35	INV yˣ	70	2nd Grad
14	CE	36	2nd Pause	71	RST
15	CLR	38	2nd Exc	75	+
18	2nd log	39	2nd Prd	76	2nd x≥t
−18	INV 2nd log	−39	INV 2nd Prd	−76	INV 2nd x≥t
19	2nd C.t	40	2nd |x|	80	2nd σ²
−19	INV 2nd C.t	42	EE	−80	INV 2nd σ²
20	2nd tan	−42	INV EE	81	R/S
−20	INV 2nd tan	43	(	83	·
22	x⇄t	44	)	84	+/−
23	x²	45	÷	85	=
24	√x	46	2nd Nop	86	2nd Lbl
25	1/x	48	2nd FIX	88	2nd Σ+
26	2nd D.MS	−48	INV 2nd FIX	−88	INV 2nd Σ+
−26	INV 2nd D.MS	49	2nd Int	89	2nd x̄
27	2nd P→R	−49	INV 2nd Int	−89	INV 2nd x̄

INDEX